CYNARA

CYNARA

DONALD NEWLOVE

TOUGH POETS PRESS
ARLINGTON, MASSACHUSETTS

Cover photo copyright © 2024 by Karen Tweedy-Holmes.

ISBN 979-8-218-37206-4

Tough Poets Press
Arlington, Massachusetts 02476
U.S.A.

www.toughpoets.com

For Nancy

He restoreth my soul.

PART ONE

PART ONE

Chapter One

It was one of those Mediterranean blue mornings that mask the deep core of horror in New York.

I went into the Apthorp, a fanciful Florentine apartment building on upper Broadway for a reading, or seance, with Roberta Winters, a noted medium visiting from New Jersey. My psychic research. Someday I hope to be the Homer—or Vermeer—of the afterlife. I've been getting messages from over there, big pictures and long descriptions of the place.

A short, svelte brunette with shocking violet eyes—a deep pure twilight—smiled with surprise and asked me to wait in the sitting room. Why was she surprised—the energy of my smile? My Homeric aura? She glided up with tiny footsteps (I felt she could glide sidewards or backwards just as easily) and handed me a flyer for a forthcoming Spiritual Frontiers Fellowship world powwow on Staten Island. Beyond glass doors Roberta Winters gave advice to an elderly couple. A bell binged. The couple came out, their eyes aglow, thanked the svelte twilight, and Roberta Winters invited me into her reading room.

The seance room looked worn and lived-in. "*Uhhh!*" she said, holding her head. "Do you have a headache?"

"Not that I know of!"

She held her forehead and seemed to stare at something beside me. "It's just—wow—I got a terrific pain when you walked in. Well, it might be my own, y'know."

I plugged in my tape-recorder. We sat in straightbacks, facing almost knee to knee. Behind her the morning window hurt my eyes.

"I guess you're well into this now, aren't you? You've been studying. Going to classes?"

"Not yet. I been reading a couple books by Arthur Ford." I was not talkative.

"Going to the Spiritual Frontiers convention?"

"I just heard about it."

"That's funny. I *see* you there—with your wife or girlfriend."

"I'll be happy to go."

About thirty-five, she's neat, combed and made up as if to go bowling. More twilight blue eyes, eaglelidded. A psychic since childhood. She finds lost articles and has worked with the police on murder cases, finding bodies. Hard to believe this is she!

"Do you believe in reincarnation?" I asked.

"It's not important, do you think?"

"I guess not. My fiancée thinks it is. . . . I've been practicing self-hypnosis."

"I picked that up on you. It's not the same as meditation, you know."

"Right. Hypnosis is going into yourself, sinking under, and meditation is being open and alert. But I do get images and messages through hypnosis."

She looked like she got lots of pictures and messages.

"Meditation is more metaphysical," she said. "I look away from you, by the way, because I *see* better." She meant spirits at my right. "I can't stand people who don't look at me when they talk to me. Were you married once?"

"Mm. Twice."

"Are you living with this girl now? Because I get this relationship like marriage. Does she have children? I see her concerned about her child."

"The, uh, child flew to Idaho yesterday to take some summer courses."

"That has to be it. A daughter. Pulling away. Being separated from her physically. Do you have a brother in spirit?"

"You mean dead? Transitioned? No,"

"I get like a brother. He seems young. Well, okay." She read more sign language from the spirits. "Also, I get only one parent with you. You have one in spirit and one living. Would this be your father that died? I'm getting a twitch with him. This has been a matter of a few years. I get sickness but rapid death."

"That would be a fair description."

"It drained his mother. Also, I get the name Arthur with you. Can you place that? Well, let it go, you may remember it later. If it's important it'll come right in."

"Arthur Fields? I have a friend who went into spirit about a year ago named Arthur."

"Did he have some kind of accident? He's in a wheelchair."

"He was wounded in the Second World War."

"I don't know the name. It doesn't seem very important, but

when they come through I like to let 'em through."

"Well. We were always friendly and he encouraged me."

I looked at her wedding ring and wondered about her sex life. Would it differ?

"Are you having work problems? I get confusion and disorder."

"Only the problems I make for myself. It's just that I have three jobs. "

"Oh boy!" Rubbing her temples. "*Uhhh!*—are you sure you don't have a headache? I don't know where I could have picked this up. You must be going everywhere."

"No. I sit home. I'm a writer."

"I don't see books. Do you write books? Oh, shame on me. Even so, I see you busy on shorter things, articles, *shorter* things."

"I handed in an article today."

"Articles are what I see with you, that length. You write by longhand. Do you like to write articles? Because I see you *busy* on these articles. You write a lot of nonfiction. I don't see you as a reformer of any kind. You're really just now going into an upswing. More intuitive than from studied academic knowledge. I see you going somewhere with this woman. I see you going overseas with her. You're going to take her with you. And you'll be there for weeks. It feels like England. I see you staying with someone you know."

"My girlfriend's sister lives in Paris."

"I see work connections."

"I was just invited over to speak. We're to stay with her sister."

"I get a strong Egypt connection with you. Why are you smiling?"

"Well, we went to a medium in Massachusetts and he told her about living in Egypt. "

"In a previous incarnation? Yeah. This may be what I'm picking up. She cooks pretty good but housework is *not* her strong point. But I like her, I get a nice warm feeling with her. She's good for you. Relaxed. I don't get any pulling apart. Also, another thing I get with you is a problem you've overcome. Something you've really worked to overcome. I don't feel you drink a lot *but*—you're laughing, you know what it is. But you overcame it because you were disgusted with it and were determined to work on it. Whatever it was, I don't see you bothered by it in the future. I do see you developing your spiritual abilities. Your girlfriend, she's more intuitive, more able to meditate."

"I think it's just being born a very sensitive creature."

Frankly, the fishing about my girlfriend and my trip left me skeptical about Roberta Winters. And casting that Arthur at me . . .

"She makes pretty good money for a woman. She likes the work. She gets disgusted with it but she likes the work. Satisfied that she's doing her thing. Is she in a profession of some sort? She's doing something of value from her viewpoint. She's doing what she wants. Are there any areas you'd like me to focus in on?"

"Oh! Do you ask questions of spirits?"

"I can ask. I may or may not get an answer. Who's *Maxwell*?"

"*Maxwell!* That's my wife's husband, uh, wife-to-be's . . ."

"Oh? Okay, we'll let *him* go, right?"

"No. There's *somebody* speaking there. His sister just died. Two weeks ago. His sister and my wife-to-be were friends."

"I get a picture of a skinny woman, not too old, maybe around fifty. I get a dizziness with her, like a pain. Did she die of cancer? What would account for a weakness right here, below the stomach? She went fast."

I named the disease.

"Oh, that accounts for it. I can't always put a label on it. Usually *they* give me the symptoms, then I have to interpret them. The way they felt when they were sick."

I was still breathless about Maxwell.

"Well, this person just seems to be concerned with letting you know that she can *get through*."

"Does she say anything?"

She was silent. "'I'm okay.' That's all I'm getting. 'I'm okay.' It was hard for her, apparently, because she wasn't prepared for it. I'm just being impressed, with 'I'm okay.' She was your girlfriend's sister-in-law? I seem to see her with her arm around a teenage girl. I get the impression that this particular girl is also in spirit. Maybe your girlfriend can place this. Who did you want to . . ."

I asked about my analyst's brother, a metaphysician and master linguist, but I said only his name. She described him and said I wanted to emulate his style, but also that he was not available. If I'd brought his picture or some article of his she thought she *might* have been able to make a direct connection.

"How about Bill Wilson?" I asked.

"Did he give lectures? This is another person you admired, is what I'm getting." She stared silently at something beside me. "You saw him several times. I get him as very busy-busy, very active. Did he go on lecture tours? I see him traveling. That's all I get on him. A lot of vitality. Was he a writer?"

"Well, in a way. He was the cofounder of A. A."

"Ohh, your problem *was* a drinking problem? I get that you've finished it, you're not going to fall off the wagon."

"No, it doesn't look like I will."

I could see Bill Wilson "busy-busy" and began to understand the hard work of fathoming spirit images and signs. She read them faster than I can grasp my own dreams. I felt rising admiration. Her cheeks shrank with work and her pupils gaped widely, the way your heart dilates at twilight.

"But this was a big boost for you spiritually. Well, you know if they don't want to communicate, there's no way I can get through. Sometimes I can't even get information *about* them. I'm just told they're not available. If they don't want to be available, there's no way anybody can get them."

"I can't forget my 'brother' Arthur. Could that be Arthur Ford? He was in the A. A. fellowship and got the idea from that of starting the Spiritual Frontiers Fellowship. We're sure spirit-brothers. Gosh sakes. May I try one last one?"

"Sure."

"A girl. She had three names—Lisa, Laura, and Cynara."

Roberta Winters gripped her temples, groaning. Her head pulsed. "Is there a reason I would pick up a lot of sadness with her?"

"Oh, yes." I couldn't forget Irene—she's the woman's editor for *Scientific American*—or stop wondering how she would take this news about her late sister-in-law. Her husband's family was hardly my business.

"She's been gone a few years. A very *pretty* person, a young woman, wasn't she? *Pretty!* I get a picture of a very pretty woman. I get her in a gown."

"I have a large picture of her in a white Jean Harlow gown from a movie I made of her."

"Did she die some kind of violent death? *Agh!! Oooh!!*"

Roberta Winters trembled in every limb without ceasing. She stared into the unseen beside me, eagleeyed, holding her head, then sat back, her violet dilating, reading, listening.

"I'm getting, 'Tell him I didn't do it.' Does that mean anything to you?"

"Well, yes. I thought as much."

"And 'I didn't want it to happen.' I'm getting this. And . . ." A siren roared seven floors below on Broadway as Roberta Winters gasped painfully again and again, shaking with a fit.

". . . I get a terrible amount of fear with her," her voice shivering, "and a terrible amount of grief. I don't—apparently she's—"

The siren ran up the building in a bloody cry.

"—having some problems—working her way through even now. *Uh . . . . . uh . . . . .* I don't know what caused her death but it seems it was very traumatic. I just get violent death and this weakness—it was difficult there and . . . she just seems to be a very upset lady yet. She was unhappy before this happened, whatever it was."

"I thought she had a vitamin deficiency, which made her, uh, a little *mental . . .*"

"Was it *considered* a suicide?"

"Oh, yes. She shot herself."

"OH, GOD! No wonder she's so upset! And I was given this violent headache—I understand now. But any kind of a violent death sometimes will cause that. This was not too many years ago, was it? She seems—" Her shaking began again, sighs and sighs. "It's funny they would let *her* through. *Uhh!* She seems to be resisting a lot of the help that's around her. Now they're letting her come through here just because there was a very close bond between you—wasn't there? And they, *uh, uh,* feel that, *uh,* by letting her come through here that she can get help that she doesn't seem able to receive there. *Uh,* she had another name too. . . . I'm trying to get a line to her . . . which is hard . . ."

Her clock binged reading's end.

"She seems—is this a romantic attachment?"

"Yes."

"And, *uh,* I seem to be getting that she's telling me that you didn't have anything to do with it. She's trying to talk to me and to you. And, *uh,* she recognizes the fact that I'm here and, *uh,* that she's coming through me."

She kept stopping, listening, reading.

"But she seems to want to impress that you didn't have anything to do with it *either.* I don't know what that means. But, *uh,* I'm trying to tell her to go with the people who are around her, so that . . . she can work her way out a little bit more rapidly. Suicide is such a difficult thing . . . '*Okay,*' she told them. "She can *see* you.

Okay, I'm going to have to let her go because it's difficult. She feels better and thanks you. She, *uh*, there are people around her trying to help her and she seems to be having difficulty receiving the help, which is why they brought her here. The reason I wasn't talking to you was that I was talking to her—trying to ask her to go with these people."

I was moved but, monstrously, still skeptical.

"Now she could see you and they feel this will be very helpful for her. Suicide is an exceedingly difficult, grave sorrow. It's a very difficult thing to work their way out of. They can do it but it takes a lot of time. She has a lot of help there. But they said it's still going to take some time. It would be very difficult for you to communicate with her for some time—they don't know how long it will take her. I would suggest that you send her prayers, because it *does* help them. This is like an energy, it's like penicillin, it's a helpful and useful thing, it's *healing*. She'll be okay, but she's only just now getting to the point where they can help her. That's all I can tell you."

"Thank you very much."

"Pray for her."

"Yes." How could I not?

I paid Roberta Winters her fee, which was small, and went home to the Village to play my tape.

Tell him I didn't do it.

Then why did she buy a police pistol? And write two dozen suicide notes for decorating the house?

Who *did* do it?

Chapter Two

I live with Irene Hesperides on the edge of the astral plane in Greenwich Village. We read aloud in bed a lot—etheric, astral, mental, causal, buddhic, solar tomes. We have adventures in bedland.

She's had this two-fireplace duplex for twenty years and through two marriages. When I first saw it—we were both living alone and had met, blindingly, as blind dates—I knew that it was too much, that fate had no place this extraordinary in store for me, and that something rarefied in her Boston-Cambridge accent revealed a creature too dear for my possessing. But—

"You're *extraordinary*," she said. And I moved in.

The apartment presented me with one kind of neighborhood magic—fancy markets and fruitstands, and my own redbrick library with clock tower just out the window—and an inner magic that deepened with twilight. She's uptown all day at that rag and I sit home reviewing books and writing articles to support my fiddling on my psyche.

"I want to meet somebody my own age," I told Belinda, a divorcée with whom I worked the phones at Intergroup A. A. center. A month later she invited me to dinner to meet Irene.

"This isn't *really* the woman I have in mind for you. She's just a stand-in." I'd never lived with a focused, adult woman and, at forty-seven, was ready at last. Irene walked into Belinda's in a green and silver outfit, dark-eyed, dark-haired, and with a musical voice gifted with intelligence, and I felt the first powerful creak of becoming unhinged.

And now, under the Jefferson Market Library clock tower's four stone gargoyles overlooking the Village flow of lower-astrals still smokebound in the Waldorf Automat (torn down during the Second World War and now housing the cool dead air of the Providential Savings Bank) and into the Jefferson Market Court House (now the library) and running in a blue and green twilight for the Sixth Avenue El at Third Street (its steel junked and sold to Japan in the late Thirties) and into the faded felt hat shops and death-lighted jeweler's now spaced by Nathan's Famous Coney Island hot dogs where fagged junkies and recent astral arrivals lounge in hazes, all these spirits unaware or unwilling to believe they are dead, killing time in sights long gone, layers upon layers of lost years lived in at once by those whose earth-impressions remain vividly bricked and windowed in street scenes past, yes, overlooking this limbo and slowly fathoming its thousand thicknesses and vanished doors where rambling astrals still climbed stairways to apartments perhaps hanging in space or torn down and rebuilt with swank white facings, or still knocked about our own two floors, Irene Hesperides and I at last were rounding out our first year.

I felt full, alert, breathing, a world to be born nodding and eddying around me. The moon rose through green evenings with one yellow star. There were immense blueblack thunder-heads, and long snowfall afternoons as I wrote. I aspired to be born into the present, really to be *here* in this apartment. During Prohibition these rooms had been one speakeasy and there still is a bandstand I'm sure Bix Beiderbecke once blew on. Below my windows I watched rags walk by in loud fights with the unseen.

When my second wife and I first moved into our Bronx apartment, it was spacious, sunny and quiet. But the paint job aged for five years and by the time she cut out for Europe, I found myself drowned day and night in a Spanish underworld of razor-edged brass dancebands, churning guitars, sobbing tenors and brainless teenage heartbreak, the same tunes repeating on auto-matic turntable arms, until a harsh sea of grindingly familiar rhythms flowed through the hallways, chwanged the ceiling, wobbled walls, pulsated the floor and slapped through screens. Somehow I'd stayed sober in there for three years, as the gar-bage noises grew, an invisible rubbish clutching the street and building until my rooms, the very atoms of the walls were shot throughout with a throbbing shriek as of a million love-driven shells rubbing their insect hulls against each other in a dry mad-ness that never quite quit even in the pre-dawn twilight—some-where one singer would spell out his pain in the lull, a soft tweeze or bleeder to carry you into your breakfast torture.

My ears were drain-grinders for broken glass and rusty razorblades and did not hear that city whose liquid sounds also played through my walls and rooms and shot shimmering hues up my building in geysers of color, the heavenly rainbow tones of that world next door which is *right here*. I knew only the unsaved in their serial marriages and shining-eyed, bone-scraping blood-screech of love or abuse—every emotion given the full force of the adrenals.

I lived in a place of thieves where kids stoned my windows daily and I could follow a family rage across my shivering bedroom ceiling, then kitchen, study and livingroom ceilings. But there were times when, to hock my trumpet or trombone, I had to enter the fire sermon of South Bronx a few blocks away, and here was a place where grief hung in the air like leafmeal, passion groaned on downpursed lips, hard sighs of idiot desire were cast-iron creases on passersby, the dead burned in the fire of birth, a fire of aging, of loss and ashes, and the lesson leaped from the bricks and paving and Third Avenue El that here was an even deeper plane of insane despair than the rocking madness of my own house. And that in South Bronx there were even more removed pockets of hopelessness, the junk-savers, crippled, diseased, bedridden in lost rooms, and the utterly mad, a seabottom where the sunlight of high noon came through as a sharp cracking on the consciousness that instantly hazed over again.

And on some like seabottom for suicides Cynara now floated, self-exiled, a prisoner among stumps of the desire-hobbled—no more the flame-swimming tease of a summer night!—but a dark being, self-stricken, stoned by a blow that resisted all light.

Who gave that blow?

The last time I saw my little coconut she wasn't smiling. It was in my Bronx apartment. She and her second husband had just returned from Italy with their baby daughter, and stopped off to see me on their way to Paradise, California. She feared that worry would end her nursing. I drew her aside to my study, kissed the years away, again pressed into the flesh and spirit that had now gripped me, on and off, for twelve years. She held my arms, her eyes pleading for some word she hoped I might have, a key to the shadows that followed her doorway to doorway on Riverside Drive—she'd told me about them some months earlier and her daughter's birth had not driven them off. I did not grasp the deeps of her fear, could not read the plea in her eyes. I thought she was asking me where our old lovelife had gone. She stood before me half paralyzed and I could not see past my personal loss as it crept in a fine fire over the hairs of my arm where her fingers moved. We went in to her husband and my wife. I never saw her again, alive.

Irene combed her husband's books from enormous shelves, boxed them into the attic, and I married my collection with hers. We were bound.

Chapter Three

Two years before she died, Cynara and her second husband had gone out to the Esalen community in California to have their souls made whole for six weeks. They returned, took an apartment on Riverside Drive, and within six months the dark shadows of drunks and junkies on nearby Broadway, and muggings, robberies and murders on their front walk, along with her private fears, had eclipsed the California sunburst.

She told me, "If you don't keep up the exercises and have a lot of friends doing them too, it all blows away." But she was planning to meet some maharishi who was arriving next day at Kennedy Airport.

The sun set rouge red over the Hudson and, through her livingroom windows, died in twilight. We were alive, alone. I'd remarried a few months earlier and was quite in love with my wife . . . I strove to tell her of my spiritual growth through joining A. A. and through the warmth of a generous elderly doctor who was helpful with drunken geniuses. I spoke, heaving and glowing, as one released from deep darkness into the morning, still blind but in the tidal grip of recovery. I did not know my worst drinking was still ahead of me, the really heart-palsying cold horrors.

She told me about her shadows. I asked her to see my doctor and even made an appointment for her. She did not keep it. Did she want to get well? We fear change more than illness. When we first met she was fourteen (I, twenty-eight) and would quote Eliot to me: "Humankind can not bear very much reality. " That adolescent melancholy was now deeply fixed, and I saw that she would rather yes glumly to his hothouse sluggishness than be reborn. Rebirth—there's no *other* way out of death. As *The Waste Land* asks,

> "That corpse you planted last year in your garden,
> "Has it begun to sprout? Will it bloom this year?"

Unreal City!

> Under the brown fog of a winter dawn,
> A crowd flowed over London Bridge, so many,
> I had not thought death had undone so many.

Eliot, the Homer of the middle astral.

For all my recovery uplift, I was still stashing varieties of pot. She said that her husband had an eye for my wife—perhaps we could all go to bed together. My spine rattled its tail. I said I'd try to talk her into it. The evening came, we smoked, my wife got sick and nothing happened, but we stayed overnight. When we awoke, her husband had gone to work and my wife was showering. I'd looked forward to love with Cynara. She was robed.

I opened it, pulled her into a bedroom and loved her while the shower ran. It was a sudden, brutish two-minute drunk that left me sober, or dry. Her eyes were in some middle region, pleading for a strength neither pot nor sex could bring.

I never told my wife and, thank God, she never asked. I get no power from adultery, and was happy not to have shared her in some pot-happy forsaking. Bear with me. I'd been in the grip of an earlier tease of Cynara's, two years before, when she was married to her first husband and I'd not been granted two minutes of flesh.

She and her first husband, living in Cambridge, invited me up for Hawaiian dinner and to stay overnight. Purposely sober that evening, but packing a gallon, I took the train and when I arrived the stove was steaming and I was mad as a mountaineer in thin air. She was bare under a net sweater through which her nipples poked. We ate on the rug, like natives. God, I felt good, burning and trembling. To serve and eat with us, she put on a lava-lava, a printed Samoan loincloth, and while we ate she was my grinning pagan coconut of old.

Her husband, Jean-Paul Sartre, whom I'd known as long as I'd known her, was already working on his doctorate in philosophy. He was still in his destructive-criticism phase and pulping out some thesis of pure nonbeing. With one burgundy, I was in the grip of the Life Force. I pulsed and hopped from limb to limb inspiredly. He eyed me sideways, trying to nab a bat or two the wine had flushed from me. I felt great well-being, gorgeous as a eunuch with his sex restored. I had passed through death into naked dreamland itself.

"I, uh, hope you don't mind, but I can't keep my eyes off her breasts."

"Of course not!" he smiled foolishly, arranging his glasses.

She shucked her net and threw it past me at the couch. He smiled familiarly at her bosom. "I'm dying of steam," she said. I looked at him coolly as Wittgenstein shuffling a verb but was white nervematter throughout my being and breathing deep gratitude that my life had made it to this candlelit moment. A light rain struck the windows.

During dinner one of his philosophy students, a short engine-like fellow with mad dark darting eyes, arrived unexpectedly and was invited to sit with us for baked pineapple-Alaskan. He sat crosslegged on the floor with us, drained, spooning up ice cream and meringue and yellow lumps, not looking at her once, even when she pulled the shades or scrubbed hot wax off her toenail, shying from the very edge of sin as he dipped into her divine compound.

The room was wet with sex and weirdly holy in the rain.

While Jean-Paul shook and scattered the weakened lad's first principles of existence, Cynara and I did the dishes. I washed, slowly, lovingly, my soap-sopped sponge wooing the china's most hidden gleam. I was not married. And would have buried myself alive for a night with her. Quietly gliding, he spidered about the livingroom to keep one eye on her wherever she moved. I dropped my sponge onto my shoe and under the sink ran my soapy hand straight into her while she dried her steamer. My heart pounded. It's so hot, she said turning to me, and rewound her lava-lava.

The dishes, ashine as my eyes, came to an end. I was dry to the bottom of my lungs. I'd just painted a fresco on my bedroom wall, a hodgepodge of famous religious paintings and statues I'd seen that summer in Italy, and was so beside myself writing its glories in the air that I offered to do a watercolor copy on her back. She got me her paints and I happily perched on the kitchen stool adorning her back. A badge of splendor, its highlight was a Pietà on her spine, the Virgin Mary mourning the dead body of Christ on her lap. There was also an Annunciation with the Angel Gabriel as a dove descending with great tidings to Mary while Joseph slept, a copy of Giotto's Judas kissing Christ, a Last Supper, a Crucifixion, a Descent from the Cross, and three angels weeping in flight, also from Giotto. I was eager to record the whole mural. She hopped into the bathroom to admire her back. I said I'd left out the Last Judgment for lack of back space. She asked me to put that on the front so she would be rainbow-bright all over. Jean-Paul saw me set to on the Trumpeting Angel and came out to see what we were doing. He was quite angry at the crucifix, since they were Jewish, growled after a washrag and scrubbed her clean in the bathroom while she rolled her eyes at me on my stool.

The student left, whitefaced, the violent wiping out of my work driving him into the rain. We settled down in the livingroom. I sat facing them on the couch, pleasuring them with my European whorehouse stories (I'd been nurse and manservant to a wealthy young Irish esthete in a wheelchair and had suggested we take Cynara to Europe with us—he'd met and admired her, wondered if she would sleep with both of us and, though I thought yes, he changed his mind, saying, "My dear fellow, taking a girl to Europe, however immoral she may be, is only hauling coals to Newcastle.") while I worked my way down the burgundy gallon. She threw off her lava-lava. They were utterly sucked in by my stories. I was dying. She went into the kitchen, returned and sat spreadlegged on the couch's arm. I brought out my Madrid cathouse with its palatial ceiling mirror, not stinting on the raunch. Idly, with unbearable slowness, she stroked herself.

At last they went to bed, after giving me sheets for the couch. I entered my tomb, sipping, unable to believe I was not at the table I had labored over, that I'd been brought this far only to be retired one breath short of rapture. I listened to the rain wash through their bedroom sighs.

After lovemaking, she ran out happy and naked and spermy in the lamplight to ask if I was all right on the couch. Half off the bed, Jean-Paul watched from the doorway, putting his glasses on. He shone with fear and triumph. I stared at her wetness. She smiled sorrowfully, even with pity, I think.

"A kiss goodnight," I said, waving at her husband.

Chapter Four

At thirty-eight I found fantasy and alcohol had swallowed me so strongly that I did not know one other person's soul, nature, habits, speech, character, or whatever I was supposed to know as a writer. Cynara was knowable but my brain was coated with June bugs whose glow I mistook for writer's bliss. To show anyone's inner being was, for me, like breaking boulders. It wasn't imagination's sublime play.

Cynara was Jean-Paul's Simone de Beauvoir in high school—the highest averages in the town's memory—her picture (*"Ugh! So Jewish."*) and valedictory printed in the local paper. Aside from overflowing genius and a winged spirit, she'd been denied wit and a gift for works, other than swift watercolors. She had endless knowledge of painting styles and a knack for ornament, cooking and clothes. To perfection! But she couldn't *sing* "Happy Birthday." Perfection throttled her. She turned out short lyrics about the embers of her adolescence. There was a talent and fellow-feeling for work with the blind and retarded—but years later she was a bust in the business of baby photography. When I secretly told a writer friend that I was running off with this fifteen-year-old, he tried to make sure I understood her limits—I saw for myself that her greatest skill was for attracting men. But her shyness, modesty, insight and beauty, when near (or far!), gave such delight that reason was pulled up by its roots. She was a fleshy miracle beyond belief, powered by fears that made her give everything, with a lovely laugh, to keep you on her thread. Sex shone so strongly that she kept her face plunged into the sidewalk.

And so much for psychological pasteboard—I didn't know her!

But she often surprised me with unforeseen blazings when something I wrote or said did not measure up to her picture of what our grand love should be. I wrote a five-act play with her as heroine, several epic extravagances and fur-lined fantasies too crazed for print, and yet I have only one phrase ("Yipes!") with which to give her life here. Twelve years, one phrase—that's not good. It's no use trying for her deepest moral and ethical soul-markings, those grave signs or germs in the spirit-mold so wonderbearing to see. She formed herself in moving men about, using her bright body as a kind of gyro for finding the true north of her being or a calm standing-room when her faults shifted at the core, as they did hourly. The body that sickened her had a worth I swore to unwaveringly. Flesh was her most useful fact, and least prized. One night, her house empty, I sneaked up to the front door to leave off my latest outpouring, and she answered in candlelight and a towel, then bashfully lowered the towel a bit (just for me!), took my sheaf of vows, slowly closed the door with an unwilling struggle, my eyes shut off after one flare of witness to her self-besieged amber being, that envied body which kept her friendless throughout high school, cursed with allure, self-hatred, self-love. She panted after my mind while I craved to ravish and find in her carnal candy shop the rewards that decks of rejection slips denied my ego—somewhere in her womb and on those breasts and in those beseeching eyes an American goddess sought me, ordering my rapt invention for that day or night until, rosy and gorged, she rose to meet my upriver rival to bathe him in my blood as she bathed me in his and others. As she moved away a straw Chinese finger-sleeve tightened to bind me still closer no matter the distance. And she had sleeves on each finger.

I wrote about her unflaggingly because the sight of long passages of words about her excited her. And made her smile or sneer—I could seldom guess which. Perhaps her eagerness was in part to learn who she was and whether I blindly might have triangulated her exact psychic location. My lovesmeared wine dreams were not bold outlines against the sky. Her face often rose to mine (we once made love in a cemetery) with deathless thoughts, deep as she could manage without forethought, as if an offhanded deathlessness might lend point to our doings. We spent a half-century searching for her first climax, year upon year, and then her first cousin found the key with a pint of Southern Comfort. He passed out and she was so tearstricken she sprayed his furniture with urine. I too was hopping mad when she told me and burst into tears on my steeringwheel. It was gone, the first joy I'd slaved to shake loose from her. Sometimes she'd lie there afterwards like beautiful cold cuts for a party never to be given. I wept against bricks. I wrote a poem, "*Sigh! but dig you must in a naked bed*"—whose meaning escapes me today. I tried wearing a rubber Frankenstein mask and yanking her hair. It nearly worked. *"So close, so close!"* she'd sigh, waiting for the big blossom. I saw marigolds. She'd wanted to come up with the roses so badly, but was frightened of the new Cynara she'd find in them. After it was too late she'd simper, "I might have. *That* time I might have."

I had an elderly hermit neighbor who liked to stand stark naked on our fire-escape (we had topfloor pads) and study the night with long binoculars like a U-boat commander. I told her about his unbelievable member. One night I passed out on the couch and awakened in the dark hearing voices. I walked into the bedroom. She sat half-draped under a sheet while my ghostly neighbor sat naked on the bed's edge. He'd seen me sleeping and just stepped in to say hello baby to her, since we were all friends. *"Hello,"* he cried cheerily, *"you're up!"* I liked this man but got angry and shoved him hard into the hallway.

"Sonofabitch! Why didn't you call out?"

"I wasn't afraid. Besides, I wanted to see. He's not so big."

I got very angry. "Right in my own house!"

"Oh pooh, darling. We were just talking. I wasn't going to let him do anything."

I knew that at this very moment he was standing with a waterglass pressed to our bedroom wall, listening, and I cried, "Fuck you, Admiral Canaris!"

I began drinking. Every meeting with her was Homeric.

"A fucking Homeric experience!"

"Don't be depressing." She gave me her lovedeath look. "You

know I love you."

Late one winter afternoon, I took her up on the Empire State Building and played "Star Dust" over the city on my trumpet. You couldn't see for the fog, so no one else had bothered to come up. She slipped off her pants. We made love standing up.

We made love in an elevator going up to a dinner party.

I wanted as much of her as I could get: Every handful came from God, whatever the time or place. Woolworth's! In her small home town, during high school lunch hour, daily, it was the only outdoor spot where we couldn't be seen—the roof of Woolworth's dime store. But she never had those long-stemmed roses.

We planned to elope when she was fifteen. It was a thorough plan, rather operatic. And it was tension and pissing in every direction and madness, which I thought happiness. I would never have this chance for a great love again—wasn't I already twenty-nine?

The elopement did not come off—I was denied that purification. Her cousin with the Southern Comfort swam by in a Cadillac and was forgiven, she left for Barnard and two years later married Jean-Paul Sartre, her childhood chum who even then had been drying bricks of logical-positivism while inching toward positive-logicalism. Later we had our Hawaiian dinner in Cambridge, and sometime after that they went West for two years. I was living in Manhattan when I got a call from her. She'd left Jean-Paul and was staying at the Albert, a lower-astral trap in the Village.

I walked over in the rain. It had rained for thirty days. The city looked runny with slime. The limbs of trees were bright green fungus. Branches, dead birds and litter everywhere in the Nazi daylight.

I sold blood for five dollars, bought a cold fifth of pink champagne, had it gift-wrapped, and went into the Albert, combed, groomed and trembling. I'd had a chest tumor of self-pity for two years, a rolling, swollen bag of tears I couldn't prick and flush. Not a tear, just endless heavy breathing. I wanted to drain it but it was like trying to cry blood.

I didn't know what was coming but I wanted to knock her up so she couldn't get away. No holding back.

Three zombies with shining eyes and cans of beer walked out, screaming in crazed Spanish. I went up to her room in the fifteen-watt hallway haze. A boy hung nodding on a wall, stuck there with flypaper. At her door, years of grief confirmed that I'd once lost someone truly extraordinary—my Garbo, my Camille.

The door opened. Her cube was lighted by a fat little candle in a red glass, the flame weaving on melt. She wore black leotards, no skirt, and a skintight black jersey. She felt much slimmer but still bosomy. Two weeks earlier she'd tried to commit suicide with pills and woke up in a rented motel room three days later and fifteen pounds light. That made the third try I knew about—one on razor blades at eleven, and pills at thirteen had landed her under a stomach pump. We made love in red candlelight. I never saw the room, it was too grim for a bulb. She said she wanted to score some pot from me so that she could make it with still another cousin. I got angry and said I wouldn't supply a rival with dope. She said I was no rival—meaning I had no long-term hopes. The cousin phoned while we were lovemaking again and she talked and laughed with him and made a dinner date. He was a very well-to-do professional man. I drank my despair to the bottom and, having two tickets to Burton's *Hamlet*, invited her to the Saturday matinee. During the matinee's intermission I told her I wasn't giving her the pot (she still thought I'd get it) and made some unguarded remarks. She moved to another row. I left, missing the big graveyard scene. I had better graves in mind, that long sleep where your muscles are sliced and you shrivel into utter peace at last.

I went on a death trip through all the hock shops on Third Avenue. I was drunk and nobody would sell me a gun. They kept telling me I wanted to shoot myself. At last one dealer sold me a twenty-two rifle for fifteen dollars. It's very hard to kill yourself with a slug less wide than a pea. It was all I could buy! I bought it. I was an ex-Marine and, if necessary, could shoot myself several times over. I welcomed the contest.

I carried the gun home wrapped in brown paper, laid it on my bed and framed it with nude woodland snapshots of Cynara she and her husband had given me and I'd blown up. The cartridge box was queerly heavy. Christ, I loved that shithouse railroad apartment and sat soaking it in like a moonstruck corpse. My cracked shoes were squishy with shirtboard. I went out in the downpour and tapped my Avenue C liquor store, whose Polish owner specialized in hijacked booze, for a case of four gallons of red. I climbed into my fungoid sheets, expecting to kill myself somewhere through the case. It would feel good to slip feetfirst into the North Atlantic and freeze forever.

When the wine backed up and got unswallowably metallic,

I got ale on my store tab. After three days of wine and ale, my apartment looked like a bottle garden and I needed more than a shave. It was still raining. My rifle had pitted in the damp and I saw rust flecks down the bore. I had no ramrod to clean and oil it. I was afraid to fire it, it might backfire and blind me. I moaned from room to room like a gelded buffalo and, in a fit, smashed half my favorite pictures with the rifle butt.

Finally I called the Albert to make up. She had checked out, into the mist.

One evening there was a knock. I'd had to get cleaned up to go uptown and earn the rent as a temporary typist. I was in a suit. She needed bolstering. I took her to hear Nilsson sing Isolde at the Met. We had loge seats, right over the singers. *Tristan* is my song. She'd never heard it all the way through but drank every note into her atoms. Every few moments her eyes, dark with feeling, joined my soul. We had champagne at both intermissions. I had to glide to keep my sole from flapping. We squeezed hands through the last act.

Over coffee, we agreed we always had a good time together. We vowed fellowship beyond love, sex and the little tenements of marriage.

Chapter Five

For six months I helped her get well. She never lacked money. Back home her father ran some dark businesses that required lending money to on-duty policemen—he toted a flashy bank- roll and never stinted on her clothes. I liked him. She made up monstrous tales about Daddy. I took her wherever she wished, always telling her, "Gee, ya look *terrific*. You've never been this lovely." And perhaps I gave her more than flattery. She always wore two or three shades of pale or coral that gave her lips an unreal beauty, the soft pink of a water nymph.

One day she phoned and entreated me to meet her at four a.m. at a bistro called Boit du Nuit just off Times Square. She had a job there. She told me to pretend I didn't know her.

Hi, she said, sitting at the bar in a black dress. There were other soft-voiced girls at the dark bar with strangers. The bar sold no liquor, only juices and soft drinks in wine glasses. *Doing anything?* she asked, smiling softly. The whole room was soft and whispery. My heart fell.

"Thanks." I sat and bought her a high-priced juice.

"How are you?"

"Oh Christ. I feel like Svidrigailov."

"Who's Svidrigailov?"

"He's the hero of *Crime and Punishment.*"

"I thought Raskolnikov was."

"That's just a cover. It's Svidrigailov who itches for little girls."

"You're feeling no pain."

"Don't be too sure. Are these, uh, working girls?"

"Oh no! We'll be fired if we make dates with the customers. This is just a place for lonely men to sit and talk with a girl for a while."

"Consultation?"

"Some of them sit here for hours. We get percentages."

Through this talk she was smiling *forlornly*, with little flarings of deep sympathy, as if we were discussing some dead wife I don't have.

"*He's* the boss," she said.

"Looks like your father!"

"I'm in a movie. It's a porno, but I don't do anything. Just a scene where I apply for a job. They're dreary, the girls. Ugh. Well, I'm dreary too."

My heart sank lower. "I'm getting together an underground movie. Maybe you'd like to be in that."

She got off and we went to Childs for coffee—she was twenty-four and ten years of men, sex and suicide had not dimmed her eye nor left a single memory on her face. Maybe she slept a lot. She looked odd, dressed in vampire-black in the bright cafeteria, the Broadway astrals slouching past our window, and said the men amused her. She was on some rubbery plateau beyond suicide but not quite alive. Marking time through one of those plastic coffeecup lulls Wagner ignores. She went home in a cab. The foggy nightsky passed overhead like batskin. I went down into the subway with the astrals. Suddenly I was not in the subway—I must have gotten off a train. I stood dead sober on an elevated platform at Coney Island and was looking out over the ocean. Wonder passed through me like a physical force and a hard swimming breeze cleared my sinus. Each pantleg was slashed at the bottom pocket, razored, my two ten-dollar bills gone. The horrible pale hearse of the train pulled in like an American meditation going *clank-crunch-crunch-runch*. I went home, sliced with twin scratches, and rent my slashed pants, mad with some kind of botulism or Black Death, then washed and shaved and went off to be first in line at the Second Avenue Blood Bank.

I searched the Yellow Pages for a hypnotherapist to help me with my smoking, overeating and drinking. Let someone else handle my problems. But I got a book on yoga instead and for a month did exercises and stayed dry, but allowed myself cigarettes. I'd stand on my shoulders for long periods in the kitchen, my beerfat sloped over me like the breast of a giantess.

Easter came. She decided to visit me Saturday evening and listen to some Bach masses Sunday morning. I laid in some wine for unlocking her roses—ten years and I'd still not gathered that bloom even once! We had a candlelight evening (I failed again), talked late into the night and, come morning, there was a very early knock on my door.

I peeked out, naked. It was a sixteen-year-old Black girl who'd run off from home and lived up in Harlem with a lesbian. She'd visited me a few times alone but I'd never got her into bed.

She stood there in a flower-piled Easter hat and sky blue new finery.

"Thought I visit you Easter morning."

"Oh, come in."

She'd seen me naked before—who hadn't? The bedroom was just off the kitchen. "This is my friend Cynara."

Cynara sat up under the sheet and the girl sat on the bed's foot, her nervous eyes abulge. I stacked the *Mass in B-Minor* on the hifi and let Easter ring loud, then gave her a wine and lay by Cynara on the sheet. It was a Dutch-blue day outside.

"You livin' here now?"

"Nope. He's still a bachelor."

"I wonders—we get along pretty well, don' we?"

"Yeah," I said.

"Ahm tired of that lezzy. She on the make for me, always."

"I can understand that. I really can."

"I wonders—I like the Lower East Side. It's so alive. An' I like you—we get along. Why don' I come down here an' live with you?"

"Well! I haven't had anyone living with me for a long time."

"I means, you go your way, of course, see whoever you want whenever you want. But I like you. I always seem to learn a lot with you, an' I think I like t' get a li'l thing goin' with you."

"What do you think of that?" I asked Cynara.

"What do *you* think of it!"

"You be your own man, of course."

Kyrie! Kyrie eleison!

"My own man . . . Well, y'know, we'd be sleeping together?"

"Oh, I could use the couch. Like before."

"The fuck you could."

"We work somethin' out."

"What we'd work out is you delivering in large bundles."

"Huh?"

"*Fucking!* Plenty of fucking. I'm tired of yoga."

"What's *yogi*? I don' smoke none of that shit."

"Don't worry about it. I refuse to spend pointless hours chasing you around the bathtub like your lez friend."

GLORIA IN EXCELSIS DEO!

"Ah don' go in for threesomes."

"You don't go in for twosomes."

Large eyes, inworked with selfishness.

"You heard Cynara. We gotta be comfortable together, if we want this apartment full of heavenly music."

"Why we have to be that comfortable?"

"Because I'm a full-blooded MALE! I can't have you walking around in here and bathing and keeping the goodies all to yourself. I want these rooms full of heavenly *bells*. Go ahead, strip."

"Ah think Ah'll go for a walk, think it over."

"There's a church on the corner."

I never saw her again. Cynara wrinkled her nose. "You can do better than that."

"She's a onesome."

We made love, or I did, then Cynara went uptown for a lunch date with her cousin. She was gone again—for a year. She married him. Gary Goldstein, insurance broker.

The three of us met one day in the Village. He'd let his hair grow and wore a droopy gunslinger mustache for her but he still supervised a whole floor of brokers in the Empire State Building. They had a darkroom in their apartment and were starting up her sideline of baby pictures. I asked her again to be in the big one-thousand-dollar movie I was at last filming. She and Gary showed up at a hall I'd rented and built a set in. I took her up to Eaves Costumes for a tight, white low-cut Jean Harlow outfit, white ostrich fan and long white boa, and several white feather caps, and shot her in an all-white room with a white cat. My crew and I shot for two days and the final, edited four-minute color film, with all its von Stroheim garishness, revealed a wounded, haunted spirit (and faint vulgarity blooming apace) I did not think twice about until years later. Under layers of "production values" to set her off as Queen of the Night, my coconut floats forth instead (as I may have meant!) as a tease supreme.

Many months later she phoned to ask me to go to court with her and Gary. I might be needed as a character witness. She'd been raped.

The court was full for the trial. The main defendant—there were three—was a six-foot-seven Spanish Black, named Reuben, with the biggest bush I'd ever seen on a man's head. It vibrated loud booming waves of hatred.

"I wanna talk! This honky shithead ain't my lawyer! An' YOU ain't my judge! I want a PEOPLE'S JUDGE!"

Gary was called to the stand and told how the three robbers rang the bell of his Riverside Drive apartment, burst in with long knives, held Cynara and himself captive, robbed them, and how Reuben had attacked her. He said he'd feigned sickness and went into the bathroom as if to throw up and phoned the police from the bedroom.

"*It's a lie! All a lie!*"—Reuben on his feet, pounding the table.

"Sit that man down and put him in handcuffs."

Cynara was called and told how Reuben forced her to submit with a knife at her throat.

"NO! NO! NO! This is a WHOLE LIE!"

"One more outburst and you'll be removed."

"This ain't MY COURT!"

She went on, adding that she was forced to blow him in front of her husband. The judge begged her to speak more loudly.

Reuben rammed back his chair, jumped onto the table, swearing he was being raihroaded and made at Cynara, "LYING BITCH! BITCH! BITCH! I'LL KILL YOU SOMEDAY!"

Six policemen carried him out over their heads, the whole length of him kicking and screaming flat in the air.

Later, he was sentenced to eight years. Cynara and Gary were dismayed. They'd hoped for twenty. With good behavior, he could be on the street in three years, a six-foot-seven fever of revenge.

The shadows set their careful teeth into her soul.

Chapter Six

She phoned to say she was in the Village and would like to see me—if my wife wasn't home. We'd not met for a year. She arrived wearing dark glasses and was in full pregnancy. The street scared her, my hallways scared her. She lay on the bed to rest her back. I read her some passages from the eighth version of a novel of mine she'd been following for years. I kissed her and was lost. We made love. She had swollen blue veins everywhere, that shone in windowlight. When I took her home in a cab, she was very nervous in her black shades.

After she had the baby my wife and I saw her and her husband off to Italy on the *Leonardo da Vinci*. The double bunk room was cramped and grim with pipes. It was not a bright ship. Perhaps the trip was to escape her shadows—she looked happy as a mother, but strained, her eyes much older almost overnight. Older and lost.

On their return, they stopped to see us, and she looked at me pleadingly in my study, silently asked me to help her get a grip on herself, and they left for California. Forever.

Their heartbreakingly beautiful daughter had Cynara's eyes.

Six months later Gary phoned from Paradise and said that

she'd killed herself with a police pistol ("a cannon"), at perhaps an hour past midnight, by an old mill in the woods near their home and in a weird cape full of stars and crescents. He found her sitting under a tree at dawn. She'd risen from bed and decorated the house with two dozen notes, dated daily over the past month, asking forgiveness and saying her daughter would find a better mother. The gun was traced to a hardware store—the clerk recalled selling it to her "for protection." She'd had the gun for six weeks. Gary said she'd recently become very calm, helpful, even happy. He felt very Eastern.

I did not cry—to avoid getting drunk—but prayed for her at the hour of her cremation in Paradise. I did not know at the time how greatly she would need prayer.

Some days later I got a call from her father. Her family now lived in New York and would like to see me. I went to see them that evening. They asked for any insights I had. I said she had very low self-esteem, a niacin deficiency that built up her fears, and had not ever done anything concrete with her genius. I did not mention what she had done *against* herself. "*I pounded the walls with my fists!*" her father cried. "'*What did I do wrong?' I kept asking myself!*" Her mother was calm, smilingly hopeful. Her father flashed his roll and offered to lend me a hundred dollars for no reason (I said no). He had two fifths and offered me scotch repeatedly. I finally drank two waterglasses of scotch and delivered a long mystical harangue about genius, her curse of beauty, and many extraordinary subjects which I pray I will not have to hear played back in the next life, though I know now it *is* on record there.

I decided to make a short film biography of Cynara, with my Queen of the Night footage as centerpiece, and I collected from her parents and Gary and others several hundred photographs, from infancy to the last weeks of life. I saw it as a twelve-minute film, with blowup after blowup, all to the Adagio from Mahler's *Fifth*, and ending on an empty swing in her childhood playground. That winter I even went to her hometown and shot the swing. The movie was never made.

One set of pictures was taken in the last month of her pregnancy. They are nudes by a girl who loved her. She is enormous, an amazing skinful of impossible, bosomy vein-lined volumes (so short and slim when I met her!), but her face is drawn and, in one headshot especially, her eyes are dimmed by an inward glassy despair that accepts death as a foregone end.

She could not know the surprise ahead.

PART TWO

PART TWO

Chapter Seven

For Irene Hesperides and me, love is shared obsessions. Only love could force me to abandon Bach, Beethoven, Bruckner, Mozart and Mahler to track down the complete operettas of Franz Lehár. We were besieged, the lovewaves pounding as we took shape in each other's eyes. After two man-eating months of soft frenzy, our second obsession—with oil, the Rockefellers and a supersecret two-centuries-old pack of world conspirators called The Illuminati—came as a relief.

By hard digging and much footwork we unburied about ten secret books on the oil trusts. The cornerstones of our obsession were the collected works of a Dr. Emmanuel Josephson (I'd met him), a fountainhead of Illuminati bloodlettings, assassinations, and empire-burnings by the Rockefellers, and a Dr. Carroll Quigley's *Tragedy and Hope*, a brilliant one-thousand-three-hundred-forty-eight-page Everest beaming a white ray into the armaments and oil conspiracy. I've no brains for this stuff but I'd been studying it for ten years. Today I was passionate only about Irene, but she was fresh to the conspiracy and eaten by anger.

"MO-*THER-R!!* You're so *suggestible!*" her daughter Laura complained about Irene's Rockefeller-Illuminati madness. She

was a Columbia senior majoring in world politics and Scott Fitz-
gerald. She'd bounded off at sixteen to live in an upper East Side
pad with a platonic boy friend "to find myself." The move was
supported by Irene, whose spirit is a disaster-relief fund.

At dawn, Irene woke me for the fourth time since midnight.
She hauled the Sunday *Times* onto our large rosefigured bed and
hooked me with a ten-minute solo, her lips knitting web upon
web of global fraud and the secret agencies of international swin-
dlers. I'd wanted a woman my own age and *had* one. Still, I found
her heavy breathing down Rockefeller's neck more listenable
than her despair over her tax problems and graphics-mad boss.
Nelson Rockefeller, arch criminal in a snarl of cartels, brought us
together and Lehár sealed it with song.

She'd look at me deathlessly from her pillow and *mean* it.
Madness, poetry, prose, that's the way it was, and kissy-kissy-
kissy with long porpoise purrings.

"Why *is* it—" I asked.

"I don't *kno-ow!*"

"—that all we think of doing is being together?"

"I think it's terrible."

"Haven't you noticed that our whole impulse is towards getting together—togetherness—sort of *being close*—"

"Do we do that?"

"—every minute that we're together we're together—"

"I think that's dreadful."

"—like pieces of flypaper."

She bounded out of bed.

"You're not going to kiss me?"

"No, we might get to be like flypaper. I've got you something special for breakfast."

"Haven't you always?"

She soon returned, glowing all over, settling the breakfast tray between us. Spiced espresso, a tin of truffles, and bowls of cold red raspberries on yogurt.

"It's *glorious* out!" She gazed at me, sighing deeply (I keep up a dike against these gazes), then it was kissy-kissy and fingers through my hair, and at last a cry, her nose on mine, "I had the most *extraordinary* dream! Dr. Josephson phoned me and said, 'It's *too late*. Since 1971 we haven't had a chance of beating them!' I saw great waves of economic discontrol rolling *wildly* around the earth. Waves, BIG WAVES!" She looked up at King Kong. "He was warning me to get a hoard of food stockpiled on the Cape. Chase Manhattan was wiped out, Federal Reserve Insurance couldn't match withdrawals, dollars were confetti, darling, nothing worth anything. All the world markets, smashed by tidal waves. The whole world was bankrupt—even Rockefeller!"

"I'm sure he still owned Venezuela."

"He didn't have the price of chewing gum. Not a *pot*, darling."

Her lovely Brahmin voice sanded each phrase.

"Who really owns the Baku oil fields? Why hasn't Russian oil ever been dumped on the common market and upset the price in the West?" She went on for five minutes. "I don't see how Rocky has time to be Vice President, run Standard Oil, and rule the world. It's more than anyone can handle in one day. Even with David's help. David's fucked up Chase Manhattan so badly. Big

Rich, Big Dumb—that's what I say. What are you reading?"

"*Flash Gordon and the Tournaments of Mango*—I once read it as a big-little book during Roosevelt's first administration."

"My God, look at the sun! Should I read the Mayer book on bankers?"

"Oh, go ahead."

"Rocky's such a snake. He's been out for the new oil reserves along the Vietnam coast for ten years. That whole war was to protect his grab. When you own everything you don't have to be President. *No more wheat thins!*—you've had five already. You're making an ogre out of me, dammit."

She grabbed the cracker out of my teeth and slapped my wrist.

"He has such an evil face, so characterless," she went on. "He's a compulsive talker—a lot of it's really inappropriate. I mean it's the whole public he's winking at at his press conferences. I think he's *craven*, as well as shrewd, dumb and wily."

"What about his collection of primitive art?"

"Those ghastly *shrunken heads*? Can't you see what they are, for God's sake?—they're people he's bought! Why did Dulles let the British lose Suez and sink British petroleum?—while Standard Oil grew. That's not *fantasy* or mysticism. That's oil. That's real."

"I believe you!"

"If he were ever exposed on nationwide TV—Vietnam oil, the federal reserve conspiracy, all the money and murder seen at last—*all of it*—it would be like the Grand Canyon suddenly splitting anew, this tremendous fissure coast-to-coast in the American consciousness—no, *world* consciousness! The whole flipping disaster."

"All right, all right! So what's gonna happen?"

She kissed me. Her dark Armenian eyes drew back, studying me, her nails raking my hair.

"Good will triumph," she said.

Our greatest obsession by far has arrived—Irene's refusal to be parted from me, even by death. Day and night and even in dreams we are magnetized to collecting domestic trivia about the Afterlife. We haven't bought a Sunday *Times* in three months.

Chapter Eight

I was in a cubistic house. I walked through a kitchen doorway on the first floor and into the third-floor attic. I was also outside the house and could watch myself flitting through its prism-faces, each doorway shifting me to a different floor or unguessable room.

Then Irene and I were in a fast truck or camper with a room in back, driving a highway on the astral plane. Standing at the wheel, I could not bear to lift my eyes from the road below with its white line. I did not dare to look out at the surroundings. No idea where we were going or what we were doing. I felt I might be driving into the rear of something moving ahead but my eyes were frozen to the asphalt. At last I just moved away from the wheel and called to Irene to drive. She was picking up in back. Nobody was steering. I stood about, the road passing. Suddenly I feared a turn ahead into nothingness or some gray prism-change that would hurl us God knew where. I moaned loudly. *There's nobody driving! Get the wheel! We're going too fast!*

Irene touched my waist. I jumped half off the bed, angered to have been wakened.

For me, happiness is high energy leveling into serenity.

The astral is not serene, nor a good place for high energy. It's so unstable that I can't bear to look at anything there—instant scene switches are too disheartening. I can never remember the method for making the place stand still and get in focus. I can't even remember I'm on the astral when I'm there.

One of the great goods of death is the absence of firetrucks. I hear the silence, the good clean silence of New York in the next world without firetrucks. We live a block from a Village firehouse. How much of my head is filled by sirens! It's a mild horror that never quite breaks down my door but never fully goes away.

I was listening to a mad Black in front of my house when a siren passed, reminding me of Cynara's visit to Roberta Winters and then of a dream of her. The Black had paper earplugs and walked by with a fingersnapping musical jerkiness, swinging and happy, talking to himself loudly. "Oh yeah, man, rubbing alcohol, that's what you need for them germs, I'm hip to that, man, yeah, yeah, I'm hip, man! Whooee, am I hip!" He was sober, talking wildly to some *being*. And Cynara—"Tell him I didn't do it," she'd said. I have a photograph of her sitting naked in full pregnancy and smiling a hardwon acceptance—a rich smile. In my five-second dream this stillness suddenly came alive. She breathed. That's all. Just sitting there—the change wasn't into live action but live flesh. I think she was impressing me that she was no longer possessed, and had a new life within her. Looking straight at me, it was a smile of extreme gratitude, or at least self-possession. Her spell crept over me, waking memories of her unbelievably sensitive nerve-charge each time I took root in her. I was lost for an hour.

True, I was sober, publishing, and given my daily bread. I'd started the ninth version of that novel I'd read to Cynara. This time I discarded the older versions and set my hero ten years later in life, since I now could give him richer goals and insight. After three months I'd found myself terrifically lacking in almost every part of what I was attempting, except energy and serenity. I couldn't get the story in focus. Much too metaphysical, an electric scrap-heap that pulled in bolts, bedsprings and padlocks. What's *this* all about? I asked myself nightly, and then fell asleep, looking for fresh insight from dreams.

I walked about in a spring rain, passing a shop where I'd once bought her chrysanthemums for death row at the Albert. I felt Guided, and thinking of the Self behind self, forgot her in the flow of damp blouses on the street, umbrellaless girls dashing from awning to awning. And at the exact moment of the perfect hour of the arranged day, I walked eroticized into my woman-filled book review office and found my hand attracted to a book that fell open to a passage wherein lay a sentence that had a phrase bursting with the very word I needed to recognize I was blind. A shiver confirmed it.

"How's this?" I asked Alice, our wolf-pack leader.

"Haven't read it. I understand it's awful." Large, moist shock and accusation. "Bishop Pike loses his glasses on the vibratory planes."

"I'm getting quite interested in the psychic."

"I know you are. I find it lamentable." She eyed me with distaste. My brain felt overripened.

Esmerelda, a blazing redhead, sat with her calves on her desk, amused by a galley. She wore a green gypsy blouse that showed her curious and otherworldly better speckles. Driven, I hunched over for a clear look at the title . . . *The Dark Fields of Venus.*

"That sounds exciting. Something astral?"

She glowed. "It's about syphilis."

"Never had it."

"Me neither." Crossing her fingers.

"If you feel it coming on, please warn us," Alice said.

I looked up our review of the psychic book and read the carnage. ". . . disoriented *stush/tush* . . ."

"What's '*stush/tush*'?"

"I don't remember any more," Alice said. "Probably *crap*, wouldn't you say?"

"I think I'll read it."

"If you must. Let us know what happened to the bishop's glasses." I took it home. It was about a Massachusetts trance medium through whom spoke the famous dead, or transitioned. Not very convinced, I skipped the beginning—which explained everything—to get to the "voices." The dead had some spellbinding moments but got vaguer and vaguer the longer they spoke. I finished, disoriented. Irene picked it up. "This is fascinating," she said. "I mean really *extraordinary.*"

Day after day she got higher and higher. She'd read what I skipped, but kept asking me for explanations.

"You're taking this seriously!"

"Don't you?"

"Ohhh . . . a bit of it."

"What part don't you believe?"

"The vibratory planes!"

"Oh, that's the easiest part. That's what really makes sense."

She read the author's explanation aloud over our Sunday tray.

"If I buy that, I'm buying a very big package," I said. I'd utterly forgotten my vision of Cynara. "Of course, it's just a restatement of the Buddhist description."

"What's wrong with Buddhists?"

"I'm from Jamestown, *New York*. Where are you from?"

"Boston and Concord."

"Oh, well, you Brahmins. Of course, most of Emerson and Thoreau stems from Hindu philosophy."

"We live by Hinduism?"

"Well, if you're from Boston or Walden Pond."

"So what's wrong with that? I'm asking, I want to know!"

"It's so *removed*. I like action. Sobering people up. Getting your inner life out on the line."

"Didn't Emerson and Thoreau *do* anything?"

"Sure. They shot down materialism, daily, by power of example. They *weren't* yogis in a cave."

"I don't understand why you're resisting this book. Why are you? I don't understand your argument."

". . . I don't either." Losing consciousness.

"Where are you?" she asked.

"The Other Kingdom."

"Where?"

"Valley of the Nile, 3000 B.C."

Irene, wideeyed. "Are you really?"

"*NO!*"

"Why don't you go to Massachusetts and interview him for *Thrill*?"

Thrill is a magazine for the sexually modern girl as she struggles through the hazes of desire.

"Honey. I don't know if they *have* sex in the afterlife."

"You could find out."

And so she lunched with the editor of *Thrill* and got me an assignment. Perhaps I could get the trance medium to pull in the vibrations of Sylvia Plath or Cleopatra or Gertrude Stein (there's no language barrier—astrals speak, or vibrate, in whole idea units, not in English or Egyptian). Whitman, Yeats, or James Joyce!—what were they doing now?

I began boning up on trance mediums and found myself once more awash in the waves of Weiser's Occult Book Store on lower Broadway. It's the world's most silent book store. Twenty-seven youthful occultists were placed like statues around the bookcases, reading. I edged about, from UFO's to Edgar Cayce, looking for the afterlife.

"May I help you?" asked a tall thin curly-headed clerk.

"I'm looking for the beyond."

"Oh. You want the Psychic section."

He led me to Arthur Ford's *The Life Beyond Death*.

"How's this?" I asked.

"It goes down like hot peanuts."

"Who is this guy?"

"Arthur Ford was the most outstanding medium of the century. He's dead."

"Transitioned?"

"Dead."

"Would you recommend this?"

"It's okay."

"But you're not mad about it?"

"Each must find his own path."

I drifted up to a statue in the Psychic section. He had wild blue screaming eyes.

"You ever read Arthur Ford?"

"Everything. He gave me a reading the year he died." He sounded hoarse and about to burst, a dreamer suddenly finding himself naked on the street. "Very accurate!"

He shook a bit, staring at me oddly, then suddenly let loose like a stammering jackhammer in the Weiserian silence. He spoke as one long pent in black print and lonely apartments. He told me how he'd raced about the country, from one famed medium to another, until he was afraid to butter his toast before casting his horoscope or phoning his numerologist.

"I'm a cripple."

"I just wanted some light reading."

"Like, y'know, a psychic cripple. I have problems."

"What about Arthur Ford?"

"Very convincing body of legitimate work. In the army he could see casualty lists before they were issued. He foresaw his own brother's death from flu. And he'd get the delirium tremens about four times a year."

"He was a drunk?"

"In A. A."

"*Ahh!*"

"But it didn't affect his control. Arthur'd get drunk but his control was cold sober."

"His control?"

"His spirit guide, a dead friend from his childhood, named Fletcher. Ford would get the horrors but Fletcher remained perfectly stable and friendly, which disproves split personality, get it?"

"No."

"In split personality those shadow selves are always vicious egomaniacs. *They* are the ones who cause the shit to fly and all the problems. That's universal, man, that's possession. But Fletcher was a model of integrity—he stuck by Arthur for forty years! Split personalities are *dreary*, you don't want 'em around."

He was ready to talk for six hours, but a girl asked me a question and I shifted her onto him. I bought the book and learned that alcoholism is a leading killer of mediums, and that mediums, who often deal with the very, very confused spirits of the newly transitioned, are sometimes themselves victims of the worst types of possessing spirits, the still-crazed addicts focused only on their manias, and abroad in the deepest twilight of the beyond.

Sounded like horseshit, but I'd heard a lot of grim mumbling in a lot of bars. And so I set out to make my dreams stand still.

Chapter Nine

Esmerelda's pale speckled cleft was ripe for my palm—and then I was lost, somewhere in a woody twilight. Late to an A. A. meeting with Jack, my sponsor. At a deserted gas station, I phoned Olympia, the girl I'd lived with before Irene but hadn't seen for fifteen months. *Pick me up in your Volkswagen!* A seven-foot blonde, only twenty-one, whose lightest look froze me. She'd driven her cramped VW to pieces. We'd spent thousands in repairs. I wanted to see *her*? Or was it that VW in which I'd spent so many hours as the victim of her tears, the ramming and jamming, out-of-gear screeches . . .

Next morning I picked up the mail and found a yellow, mis-addressed City judgment against her. She had seventy-two hours before the collectors came for the VW. A prickle crept over me. After fifteen months, I'd dreamed of this car just hours before getting a warning letter about it.

We found that everywhere we turned we were meeting psychic people daily—close friends who kept their abilities secret, until we mentioned what I was working on. A Village woman editor told us, "Oh, *I'm* psychic. So's my father—he often tunes in on me. If I have a problem he calls me up from Colorado and tells me what to do. He just *tunes* in. I often meet psychics who are trying to read my mind—I just jam them out with music or noise, and smile." She was also visited by the ghost of a murdered girlfriend whom she hadn't particularly liked. Then two friends phoned to say the ghost had visited them too. The three compared notes, but only up to a point—since one of the two friends had been the murderer. It had been a psychic murder, rolling a car, and justice was not likely. The murderer was now a respected parapsychologist with many high-flown books about his work on trance states, mind-reading and divine depths of awakening.

Irene remembered experiences with her mother's shade hanging about for a year. At last Irene cried out, *"MOTHER, I'M ALL RIGHT NOW! YOU CAN GO AWAY!"* And she did. My own experiences tumbled from the attic. And my mother's—her sister had seen their father's ghost smiling in the kitchen doorway one morning. I'd loved him and could believe it. Nearly everyone we talked with told us something. There is a vast psychic subculture walking around in silent fear of ridicule.

Soon I had a library of over a hundred books on the afterlife. A great body of exquisitely fine research in India, Alaska, Brazil and Lebanon suggested that reincarnation was by far the likeliest answer to certain cases. I followed the latest lab work in parapsychology and met Spiritualists, mediums, clairvoyants, dowsers, out-of-the-body trippers, and even a man who'd walked on the moon. There's no air-tight certainty to any psychic events (if you don't count moonwalking), but I was moved by a softly spoken passage Tolstoy wrote when he was eighty—"The dreams of our present life are the environment in which we work out the impressions, thoughts, feelings of a former life. . . . As we live through thousands of dreams in our present life, so is our present life only one of many thousands of such lives which we enter from the other, more real life . . . and then return after death. Our life is but one of the dreams of that more real life, and so it is endlessly, until the very last one, the very real life—the life of God. . . . I wish you would understand me; I am not playing, not inventing this: I believe in it, I see it without a doubt." I found some paths of parapsychology riveting, but tiring, then deadening. I wanted a world more lively.

I took a course in biofeedback and found how concentration and meditation differ. My teacher was a warmly thoughtful Catholic my own age, an atheist turned occultist who told me of his guilt over adultery. Meditation, I learned, was a relaxed clearness without pictures, thoughts, or even lingering flashes and lights on the eyes. As long as I kept clear, the box patched to my earlobes and skull gave a steady beep. The slightest focus on anything, even a soft retinal burst, stopped the beep. I was allowing my deepest thoughts to free themselves from the seafloor, rise worklessly, and pop about on my brain without thinking about them. Not receiving them consciously seemed pointless, which was the point—complete restfulness and to know without looking. I complained that I valued hard-burning work more, the strong strange pictures springing unbidden from tense effort. He said that concentration and meditation were two ways of getting to the same place, some spinal fountain that released ideas stored in my genes. I was plugging into my great-great-grandfather's spine, or into an endless nerve cord going back like twined cable to my earliest forebears, my genetic origins. My spine was the family album. I felt that to awaken this cord took an effort of fantasy that went against meditation. On another box that beeped ever harder the harder I focused on breaching the astral, I ran the beep to its limit and found myself in a chair in Irene's office while she was phoning someone, her face drained and serious and then found myself racing through her office halls, in and out of many rooms, hovering over my beloved Xerox copier, which somehow made my being in her office more real. By not working so hard to be in her chair, that is by relaxing in the halls and Xerox room, it was easier to be in the chair. At last I saw some point to meditation and the answer that came without effort.

We drove out to Cape Cod to visit Irene's dad, who lived with his oldest daughter and son-in-law. The Cape lay stormbound in twilight. My first meeting with this branch of her family—I was nervous. They lived in a low brick ranch house that wavered in a gray enclave of the astral. As we sat in a cool picturewindow glower, I felt some kind of bloodclots breaking loose and my energies seeking a friendly line to her folks. Irene had asked my promise to avoid "upsetting" psychic chitchat, but then plunged straight into it herself, a mare bolting. Her sister, it happened, had read all the popular psychic books in the town library and been pondering the supersensible walls of her house for ten years. Would she have this dwelling in the next life? Her eyes shone, perhaps I had the key. Her husband, an arch cynic, laughed, sighed nervously, then told several stories about his early naval career which were entirely psychic without his knowing it even as he told us. It was like watching a man work a calculator while denying arithmetic. Dad smiled and smiled, an eighty-nine-year-old Armenian who still drove his own Mercury, and revealed a store of events all pointing to spiritual affairs in his life and saving visits by the Above—"I never talk about them. It was God. How can you talk about God so anybody believes you? I just smoke my cigars and look out the window—*these windows*, darling," he said, pointing to his eyes. His eyes were hazel and silver in the rainlight.

Irene's brother-in-law suddenly threw up his hands, shook his head and went out to clean the garage. "*Rain* is the best time there is for gettin' a pesky chore done." When I went to the bathroom I saw him oiling and sharpening his garden shears under the bare garage bulb in a truly weird cubicle of the beyond.

Her sister began pumping me. She was ready for worlds more bold than I knew about. I talked to Dad instead. He'd sold his business and retired only a year before—a candymaker, he invented the modern marshmallow and, he says, through divine guidance at that.

"Spiritualists have these one-time happenings that can't be repeated in the lab," I said. "Well, sometimes they can, the spirits will talk on demand. Most often the medium works in trance and can't recall a word said by anyone, flesh or spirit. He's only a channel. Sometimes the spirit talks through the medium's voice box, or to one side of the medium's head, or through automatic writing where the spirit guides the pen. Or the electric typewriter! *Whole books!* Some mediums find lost articles, kidnap victims, buried bodies, or they dowse for water or oil wells."

"Standard Oil has a dowser who hasn't missed yet!" Irene

cried.

"How do you know?" Dad said. "Whom did you ask, dear?"

"Oh, we met him! But it's a secret."

"Does Rockefeller know about it?"

"Of course he does."

"Well, anyway, most spirits have dull messages," I said, "since most messages come from spirits too stupid or confused to get out of the lower planes. There's a sort of basement over there, or cellarworld or spiritual trash-heap for unregenerate drunks, junkies, suicides, murderers and so on. We have a whole shelf of books dictated by spirits describing the conditions. You wind up among people on your own wavelength, and that can be satisfying or awful. There are religious bigots who still band together over there and deny everything they denied here. Some folks don't believe they're dead and prefer to think they're dreaming or even insane. Some resist help and put themselves into a death-sleep that is very difficult to break into and may last for centuries. Frankly, it sounds so crazy that it's hard to talk about. We could send you some scientific books, but they're pretty dull."

"Oh, no! That's more my line."

"We like the more anecdotal stuff."

"Tell Dad about the son of the Bishop of Canterbury."

"Oh, that's too much," I said. "This monsignor, the bishop's son, had never had any truck with Spiritualism when he died in 1913. He was so surprised and irritated that the Church hadn't told him the truth about where he was going that he spent forty years preparing to dictate *two books*. Which we have. Hundreds of pages about the planes and spirit-bodies and spirit-places, textures and colors, really thorough—everything's there, Armenia, Cape Cod, we carry our earth-impressions with us so vividly that it actually affects the vibrations of the place, we shape places through thought-power, everything roachless and idealized—no toilets necessary. You get just what you've earned or deserve. The monsignor's picture is rather monotonously serene. But we have dozens of these books and they all describe exactly the same place or plane. We have three by a spirit who claims to be William James. But all these books seem fragments of the truth—there really is a next world and it's right here in this house."

Irene's sister agreed, nodding heavily in triumph, glittery-eyed.

"Can I have my cigars?"

"If you want them, but they won't have the same taste or lift. And the drunk gets no lift from champagne. Everything is apparently made of something called elemental essence, a mental building material that resists decay. It's a *stuff*. And the sun gives off a silver sheen that passes through everything but casts no shadow. Your humidor has an artistic completeness that its earth-artisan intended but couldn't achieve, so do poems and paintings, or faucets or this couch or the bookshelves. The monsignor's own books he'd written before passing on—they only agonized him with their conventional dogma. Whatever you write you have to live with. It's a chastening idea."

"What is?"

"Not being able to change a word you've written. Your books go right on influencing people and you can't do anything about it. Makes you think twice, Dad."

"Would you change anything?"

"I'll find out when I get there."

"But why do you believe all this?"

"Well, some it's very convincing! Not air-tight, but persuasive. There was a book published in 1916 called *Raymond*. Raymond was the son of the president of the British Society for Psychical Research, Sir Oliver Lodge. And at twenty-six, Raymond died fighting in France. So, about eleven days after he transitioned, he began sending back dictation, because he knew his father *expected* it of him. He was still pretty foggy over there, and not too happy, but he knew just what standards of evidence his father required to consider the dictation beyond fraud. He dictated fairly specific descriptions of the other side through three different mediums who were apparently not in cahoots with each other. Sometimes Raymond would send material that didn't make sense until it was collected from all three mediums and read in a piece. Sometimes Sir Oliver would go anonymously to the mediums and each would bring in Raymond who would go right on dictating, picking up where he left off with one medium or the other. The mediums were simply channels for this flow of evidence. Sometimes Sir Oliver would send an absolutely anonymous stand-in to a medium, a person the medium could in no way connect with him, and the spirit would show up and say *Raymond here* and go on with his descriptions, which the sitter then took to Sir Oliver. This method is called cross-correspondences and over the past eighty years tens of thousands of pages of this evidence have been published and analyzed to bits in these very stuffy British and American psychical journals.

There's so much material nobody could master it anymore."

"But why haven't I heard of it if it's so convincing!"

"Dad," Irene said, "you were making marshmallows."

"Ah, so I was, my dear. The best in the world, ha ha, don't forget that!"

"What's most moving about Raymond," I said, "is the picture he gives of fresh arrivals despairing because they're being forgotten so quickly by their friends and family. Just when they need prayers, nobody's sending any. Our brainwaves have measurable force, Dad. Prayer is energy. It really revitalizes."

"Now *that* I can believe," Dad said.

"Watch out! If you surrender one atom, the rest will follow."

"Ha! We'll see about that, my boy."

But we'd reawakend something. He looked refreshed, eager, fearless. His wife had transitioned thirty years ago.

Chapter Ten

We rented a car and drove off into the greengold hills of a Massachusetts summer. We'd met the medium through whom the famed dead spoke. And now we were off to find his farm in the hills.

"Speaking of the famed dead, E. L. Doctorow looks like Shakespeare," I said suggestively—she'd been mooning about death.

"It's too bad we don't know Shakespeare's birthmarks. Then we could check."

"Ford says there's no elite over there, the famed are level with the unsung."

"That should be a relief." She was reading. "Thomas Edison died while building a radio to the astral. . . . *My God*, I had the most amazing dream last night! I was in a barn with the bride of Frankenstein. She was radiant and giving me this impish, knowing smile. Really lovely. And she was decking my head with pine cones held together by Christmas ribbons—fantastic! I seemed to be the center of a celebration. Then I saw that a baby lion was being passed around from hand to hand. I kept rescuing and patting it. It seemed to be *my cub*. What do you make of that?"

Silence. "I'd rather not say."

"*Tell me!*"

"Quite frankly, you seem to see yourself as the Virgin Mary."

She was thoughtful. "I've had variations on this dream for twenty-five years."

"It's too bad we don't know *her* birthmarks. I dreamed about Tony Tripi out in California last night—hadn't heard from him in a year—and this morning I got a letter from him."

"*Hm!*" Her eyes rolled. That morning I'd picked up the phone before it rang and begun talking with her in her office.

We turned off the main highway towards Hampshire College. The woods shone, green and healing to New York nerves. Even the rent-a-car seemed to glide on a sigh.

"And I had two more dreams," I said. "I dreamed that I willed it to be a sunny blue day and it was. I was naked and holding two green weather balloons. They were tied around each ankle. I was floating and could guide the balloons by pulling two strings. Suddenly I was afraid that if I went up too high, I might fall to my death. But I liked floating and taking the risk, and I sat or hung in the air gliding over buildings. I'm too high!—maybe I'll never get down again. But I had to let go of the earth to find my path."

We stopped at Amherst. Irene's daughter Laura was visiting her first cousin Keith from Paris and we were taking them both out to Cape Cod to visit Dad. She was giving him maneuvers for life as a freshman coed.

"So how do you like co-education?" Irene asked him.

"It's incredible! I can't get used to it. Everyone's so big," Keith said. "Boys and girls both, so big-boned. Everywhere I walk, it's like I'm spying on another race. And my courses!—I'm taking 'Principles of Madness.' You can't get freshman course like that in France."

"Speaking of madness, Mother—are you still reading those *books*?" Laura is a true-blue girl massacred by an open heart. She has almondshaped, raincolored eyes, blue-brown and sometimes so sad she can barely look out of them. She's shorter than Irene, and fairer, with a changeable round face that flashes long and thin, a rising shape within. She laughs from her heart but mostly feels the pinch of reason, a mauling by abstractions, the need for *Scientific American* standards. But the first real word she ever said to me (she'd asked for advice on dividing her time) was, "*Please* don't try to organize me!" She can wear anything. She has a deep mysterious closet I peer into—the light's left on for days—and sense rich layers of sturdy fabrics. She wears French-cut, bodyshaped slacks, never jeans. She has never been out of her body.

"Worse," I said.

"What's that mean?" Laura asked.

"Oh, we've got one on tape."

"It's incredible," Irene said. "By a one-hundred-and-forty-eight-year-old man."

"You gotta be kidding!" Keith cried. "That's a hundred and thirty years older than me. I can't believe it! You mean you *really* have a tape by a man a hundred-and-forty-eight years old? I can't even think back that far—what was happening, the Middle Ages? I mean when he was born?"

Laura sighed. "*Mother.* I mean, how do you *know* he's a hundred and forty-eight years old? You mean he just *says* he is and you believe it?"

"I gotta hear it, " Keith said. "What's he talk about?"

"We have it with us," Irene said.

Laura stared hard at the countryside. "Please wait. I don't want to hear it."

"Why not?" Keith asked. He swept back lank black hair of the young Abe Lincoln. He'd been stringing a new twelve-string guitar since flying over a month ago and was still stringing it as we drove. Irene had slipped him a Theosophy book, *Man Visible and Invisible,* during his stay with us. He'd bought his own chart *astrologique* (a twenty-foot computer printout) just before leaving Paris—at eighteen also leaving childhood, adolescence and his poet mother and agronomist-stockbroker father. The horoscope was in French and we pored over his *ordinastral profil psychologique, rythme annuel, et calendrier astral* for hours while he translated and Irene made the crooked places straight. He'd lived abroad all his life and this was, perhaps, his chart of the New World. "Why not, Laura? This is so—so Poesque."

"I don't want to hear it. That's all. Just because Mother—oh, I—I—What does he *do*? Does he *say* 'I am one hundred and forty-eight years old.'?"

"Play it, play it!" Keith shouted. "This is what I came for!"

"No," I said. "No disharmony, Keith. Later."

"Oh, go ahead, play it. But if I can't bear it—"

Keith read the cassette label. "*Bishop C. W. Leadbeater: Introduction to Theosophy. Recorded April 23, 1975. Adyar, India.*

Where does it say when he was born?"

Irene started the tape. Soft flutes and drums began with a skirling pipe weaving cobralike-on-a-cloud-at-twilight. A mellow quavering voice spoke.

"Welcome to the path to the Masters. As an initiate taking his first step, there is much you should know. Let me give you a few general words in description of what you may expect to be studying."

"*He's* a hundred and forty-eight, Mother?"

"It is a path I have been on for one hundred and forty-eight years in this incarnation. Yes, I was incarnated for this term of my karmic wheel in England in the year 1847. As a child I was troubled by strange sights of people seemingly out of their bodies for a spell, and of figures with no bodies to return to. Few know, and I certainly did not, that dreams such as these are real experiences. And that dreams themselves are real, for the most part—very very real indeed. Not only was I troubled by spirits in my parents' house and abroad in the thoroughfares, but also I saw myriad colors around strangers and acquaintances alike. These I learned later were the auras we bring with us from the astral plane and which, amazingly, are the energies that produce the physical form."

Laura whitened. "Now wait a minute, fellas. I don't believe him. I simply don't."

"But such a beautiful voice," Keith said. "So tender."

Irene opened her purse and handed some color Polaroids to Laura. "So?" Laura asked.

"Everybody has two energy bodies," Irene said. "These are

the fingertips of our *etheric* bodies pressed against film with a mild electric current flowing through it. They were taken in the dark."

"But—I mean—how do you know this isn't just a picture of *electricity*? I mean, etheric body—why etheric body? Even I can see it's only electricity, Mother."

"Well, there's a big fight about that," Irene said.

I let Irene swim for herself, which she does like an Olympic star. I strive at all times to show a granite-browed earthbound profile to my future step-daughter, since her American Studies major avoids the rise of Spiritualism in the States.

"*Ugh!* I'll bet," Laura said.

Keith eyed our fingers' blue discharge. "You really can see it."

Irene was half into the back seat. "They've proven that every living body has a bioenergy field that can light up a tiny vacuum tube. This tube will light up against your skin, Laura, just naturally, without any other source of power."

"Light up a tube?—okay, I buy that. But auras—*colors*—"

"Oh, we've seen that." I jumped in. "Haven't you ever seen the purple halo around chrysanthemums? Or a light around trees and buildings in the late afternoon or at dawn? They get halos. This bold light scribbled over everything against the sky. Look at a roof or chimney around five o'clock, look a little above, and they'll have a bright outline. Haven't you ever seen a house *shine*? Without its lights on? That's the way it is all the time on the astral plane. Did you ever hold a heavy ball of tinfoil and see it glow? Or cut into a ball of lead?—the cleft is like radium. You've seen these things. Well, people shine too and you can be trained to see it."

"Can you see it? she asked.

"*Yes*—it's health! It's animal spirits. Vigor! It shines! That's what's wrong with depressed people. No shine! It's a—you have to relax your eyes to see it. You don't look directly at somebody and expect to see him shining. Usually you need a dark background for people. You look off to one side of the person and relax. Sort of focus six feet past them. Do this for a while and—give yourself time—maybe not the first day—but you'll see the colors. All sorts of aura."

"You guys aren't just pulling my leg?"

"Laura," Keith asked, "would a hundred-and-forty-eight-year-old man pull your leg? Be reasonable."

"*Reasonable?* Mother, what do they think at the office of your new interests?"

"They tell me, 'Now, Irene, keep your feet on the ground. Don't fly away.' But they're getting a little interested themselves. The secretaries are fascinated—they're all into reincarnation."

"*Reincarnation!*" Laura cried.

"Darling, Thomas Edison died while building a radio grid to send and receive from the astral plane."

"Mother, Thomas Edison died nearly a century ago!"

"No, about fifty years. I'm only trying to make clear how everything has its own vibratory rate, even the bioenergy field that leaves the body after death."

"I see." Clearing her throat heavily.

"So do I!" Keith said. "Let's hear some more Leadbeater."

Bishop Leadbeater beamed on, jovial and twinkling. "My

own Master Kuthumi, to whom I am united by unbearable affection, has kept me in my mortal frame especially to bring this message to fresh initiates. We see the divine aura unaidedly—that two per cent of one's energy body that shines beyond the skin. It is a glow, or aura, from the main body fused with the physical body. The physical body, like the moon, eclipses this invisible sun within—but that packed light *is* there!

"When we sleep it is the energy body that needs refreshment and strengthening, since this is what gave original life and form to the physical body. The energy body forming us has descended from a greater mental plane through the astral into the physical, much as an impulse (mental) precedes the blueprint (astral) that gives shape to a house, in our case the physical temple of the body. For recharging, this vital original in us disengages itself slightly (as the body idles out of gear in sleep) and absorbs energy from the invisible energy world fused with our world. During certain stages of this dislocation we dream that we are in the second energy world, which is almost identical with the physical, except for twisted distances, perhaps—distorted rooms and spaces, and like oddities. It seems an unstable place, and it is! After transition—and even before, during dreams—our first job is to learn how to keep everything *stable*. If I may draw the veil for a moment—many who suffer instability on earth face sheer horror over there, with their fears creating terrifying thought-forms: this is why Master Kuthumi warns of our need to get *in focus* in our present life—it is so damnably much harder to work on ourselves over there while fighting fears and instability. Our root fear is ignorance that if we ask for blessing from above, we will get it—but not through maniacal prayers that are themselves based on fear. What we need is surrender to a good God who gives peace and release from suffering, if we ask for it. The events which make us suffer may not change, but our attitudes will, the more we accept the serenity offered. This also gives a shield against possession by spirits, who need sympathy and release from their own ignorance. They don't *have* to suffer their ignorant possession of a mortal.

"As I say, the confused dark, the healing starlight, and the brighter astral planes are real places, attested to not just by mediums and occult books but by every major world religion and their prophets and messiahs, and they are places based on different, higher, rarer energy systems than the coarse energy and matter we measure by radio frequencies and the atomic table. Radio waves pass right through us with messages we never hear, as do television signals, or waves: we live in a sea of sounds and images we aren't aware of. And when we dream, the spirit really is in energy places that not only exist unseen in daily life (by most of us) but also are places in which we can share our energy lives, or spirit lives. The human body and its energy aura die at last, but they have within them a third, more lasting, organizing force called the astral body. This passes, with our earthly impressions and values still strong within it, into the half-world where we learn at last really to focus our beings for a greater life in store."

Laura shook her head and nudged Keith. "You better buy this for your 'Principals of Madness' course."

We drove into Turner's Falls where lay long blocks of joined identical houses for woolen-mill workers, many of them empty for decades since the mills had closed down—a place untouched by time since the Depression. The town hovered in a vast sigh. We drove over a high bridge spanning a huge arced steel dam that poured water into a breathtakingly deep basin of layered rock which could have swallowed every building in town and hungered for more.

"Do you feel what I feel?" Irene whispered worriedly.

"I don't believe it. This is the Bermuda Triangle of Massachusetts."

"Let's hope we can drive out again."

"Mother, whispering isn't polite."

"Shouldn't we stop and eat, my dear?"

"I wouldn't even want TO DIE in this town."

"I need coffee," I said and stopped by a diner. The kids went for takeouts. "Just like New York," Laura said, "no restaurants."

Irene dragged her mouth. "I wonder if this place moves around on the maps."

"Hm. I had another dream last night, an anxiety dream. I was falling forward, unable to control it—it's really strange to lurch forward uncontrollably in a dream—and something had risen out of my back. The something was a naked ten-year-old boy trying to get my attention beside the bed. I ignored him. He groaned. Then he floated lengthwise over you and lay down in your body. But he seemed to realize it was too long for him, that he didn't know how to fill it or what to do with it. Then you moved and with a *deep* groan, a rattle in his throat, he detached above you, shriveled fast, and disappeared in a wisp. He seemed in great pain."

"How terrible. I didn't feel anything. Do you think it was real?"

"I sure do."

The kids climbed back in with coffee. Keith began sucking a straw. "Coke!—*vin de campagne.*"

Laura stared at the wide main street, shivering. We still needed directions and parked in an alley behind a psychic hall called Ammal's Gardens. It was closed. A sixteen-year-old boy, solid with grease, worked on an old Ford. I asked this grease creature if he knew where our medium lived. The kid's mouth worked, his eyes intense, but he seemed unable to talk and said nothing. A heavy woman in loose droopy nylons limped up the alley on a cane. She looked drained and was talking to herself.

"*Cataclysme de campagne,*" Laura said. "Mother, I may FAINT before we get out of here."

We went to another psychic hall called Renaissance Church. It had a tiny Alice-in-Wonderland entrance in an alley, with a sign WATCH YOUR HEAD. Carpeted wall-to-wall, red plush chairs and deep couches. A babyfaced youth with wispy mustaches and hounded eyes drew a map and gave us precise directions to the medium's farm.

We got lost. The woods were ferny emerald murk, roofed with high branches. We drove over a tiny bridge glowering on a tiny stream.

Irene declared, "I've got déjà vu."

"Been here before myself."

"Wow," Keith said. "I feel we're on a raft!"

Night fell. We were still driving around dirt roads. At nine-

thirty, under a starry bowl that shone with an infinite drudg-
ery of lights into the deepest corners we could see, we found the
farm. A moonless hill sloped into starlight.

Durwood, the medium, a spare gray smiling man, his sunken
cheeks pitted and deeply creased, invited us in. "I knew you were
out there somewhere," he rasped. The livingroom was a tangle of
big dogs, cats, kids watching color TV, a parrot, and a long mon-
key cage. His eyes had the weird dull sheen of lead and seemed to
be reading our thoughts.

We sat in his study for the visit or interview. He told us
about a school he'd started in the area to teach "unstructured
learning, cosmic education. We're trying to save kids from having their heads crushed stiff in the local schools, so they won't
be embalmed in materialism and miss the real life of the spirit.
Material man has run dry. There's a whole new mind aborning.
I'm serious. You don't believe in any of this, do you?" he asked
Laura. "That's good, that's healthy. But *he's* beginning to. Right,
Keith?"

"Durwood, I'm an escapee from the most rigid educational
system in the world. A Martian could devise something better.
But—I just got to this country and it's—it's so strange. Do *you*
see auras?"

"Very clearly. You have a tender rose aura, very sensitive and
receptive."

"What's Laura's?" Irene asked.

"Oh, Mother!"

"Orange and green. She's worried about someone far away.
Maybe out west. She has to make a decision about this person, I

don't know what, maybe to visit him. Or marry him! I see her on a plane flying west."

"But I just got here. From Idaho."

"You must want to go back," Durwood said.

"I'd rather have Idaho moved to Michigan. Can you manage that?"

"No, I can't. But about auras. If you could look and see yourselves as colors, as energies, and see that every atom, every organ in your bodies, has its own frequency of vibration—if you could see it, you'd probably pass out on the spot. If you realized that every one of those atoms had to function at a specific second with all the other atoms to allow you your animation, and then you saw where one thought either helped those atoms in their radiance or short-circuited them through your depressions, or your wants, or your dreams, or your constantly criticizing, or judging or scorning your fellow man—you'd see how this defeats the atom's purpose."

"My head's spinning," Keith said. "I can't take it all in."

Durwood nodded. "You feel an incomplete vibration from former lifetimes. That's all."

"That's debatable—but leave it to the intellectuals. Do you do astral travel? And have out-of-body experiences?"

"All the time. Whenever I go into trance, I leave my body and go up to the temple of the masters. I'm not here during trance. My body is taken over by a spirit. I step aside spiritually and my control, Doctor Heron, takes over. He does all the talking—I don't remember any of it."

"That's *so* fantastic," Keith said. "It's so—*hard to believe!*"

We taped for three hours. I said the point of my article was that death isn't important, that I hoped to give the reader a sense of the other world so Homeric he could almost touch it. He smiled, somewhat surprised at my eagerness.

"We live in a universe of life, so how can we say there is any death?" he asked.

Then he went into trance for Irene and me, sort of falling asleep behind his desk until Doctor Heron moved into his body. Suddenly Durwood leaned forward, his eyes closed and face crooked in forefinger and thumb, and a strange large warm somewhat British voice boomed out of him. The "dead" doctor's spirit told us about our health, revealed who our spirit guides were, then told us about our past lives together in Egypt and Rome and during the Civil War, when I was a doctor and Irene my nurse. The reading lasted a half hour, then the doctor bade us farewell and "peace profound." Irene arose, sloe-eyed, Egyptian.

Durwood awoke after three minutes. He had no recall of what Doctor Heron had said—"I get sick of it. Don't want to know. You work with it." Shot, he smiled, and offered to put us all up. We thanked him and left.

We drove under the stars to Cape Cod, the tape-recorder on, listening to our past lives unroll.

As we were leaving the farm house, I'd asked him, "What about astral travel? How do you do it?"

He stared at me fiercely. *"Stay out of it!"*

Chapter Eleven

My adoptive nephew Arnold Grinspoon phoned from the street to say he was coming right up with "Ruby Voodoo and Pizza Bizarre, Uncle Ernest!" I dreaded him. But sometimes I feel I have to speak up to God for Arnold.

Years ago, after a 3-D pancake at the Orpheum, I turned to find a man sitting behind me so familiar that my nerves stood on end. My double. I sat wondering about my mother's sins. He was leaving. I questioned him about his family. He turned out to be eleven years my junior, but our likeness mystified even him. We also lived within blocks of each other and he'd gone to college in Cynara's hometown.

Drink bound us. He dubbed me uncle (after Papa Hemingway), swearing by every word of my marijuana metaphysics— my every pot flight was dogma. He'd chew some vision over and after a month ask for its latest working out. He became a wildly hairy playground director on Staten Island—kids called him Wolf Man—that hair bunched and sloped like a grass igloo. At last I quit drugs and juice. He began tripping in and out of asylums, growing ever more matted.

My last drunk was in his company. I'd been sober awhile

when he came to tell me his father'd died. Arnold felt nothing. He invited me to the funeral. We went out to Roslyn together for the services but stopped in a bar on the way and I got drunk trying to work some grief into his stiffness. He still felt nothing. Short of grabbing him, I tried mightily to shake some grief into him. "Save your breath, Uncle Ernest, I can't hear you. " His eyes, my eyes. "Listen! D'you want to go crazy again?" Suddenly he looked at me, burning ice. I gasped as an unseen wind shot from him into me, and I burst, stabbed. His tears. I turned crazed with grief, his grief, and fell over the bar with huge sucking cries. Next I knew, I was flickering in and out of blackout, hitching to Manhattan, reeling with sobs.

Since then I'd only talked with him on the phone, spinning hour-long hypos of uplift. Sometimes I could cut through his cloud.

The very hall prickled as he galumphed upstairs with a tenor sax, followed by Ruby Voodoo with a boxed pizza. She was gowned in silver, a Black Arabian princess. He said he'd found her crossing the street at a traffic light, talked her into his car, then taken her out and bought her this outfit. They'd been living together for two days. She was just short of speechlessness, a walled-in soul wandering about Roslyn with no home. They smoked pot at Arnold's mother's, drank beer, and sat in a madhouse for two listening to signals Ruby's brother, a prince, radioed them from Saudi Arabia.

"He wants us to come over, Uncle Ernest. But wait'll you *hear*. There's more to it."

"Can't I get you something?" I asked her bent head and black mat.

"She doesn't drink. She only fucks."

Arnold now wore Ben Franklin half-spectacles and his bunch bound in a ponytail. We no longer looked alike, only our eyes. "Aren't we twins!" he cried at her. She nodded whenever he spoke or asked her "*Right?*"—and kept face down with a super-conscious grin.

"Where's your new girl?" he asked.

"Mount Palomar. She's trying to crack those radio signals from Jupiter."

"Oh? That's a bad scene, Uncle Ernest. She should be here with you. Cooking, sewing—you got a hole in your shirt."

"It's just a rag."

"Oh? Signals from Jupiter, huh? Very interesting. Can she handle Morse code?"

"They're not sending in Morse, Arnold. Nobody knows *what* these signals are."

"Even so. We might be able to use her, Ruby. Right? You think she might dig Saudi Arabia?"

"She digs Cape Cod."

"We could give her her own radio station. Fabulous equipment. Only the best. Maybe she could learn cryptography."

I shrugged. He spread fresh-ground raw peanut butter on his pizza slice. "Protein is very important. I'm watching my health, just like you said. I only drink beer now. Burgundy makes my teeth too sharp."

My eyes pulsing at me over his half-rims. "Princess Ruby and I are going to head the biggest radio station in the world and we

want you with us—right, baby? I've designed the tallest antenna
ever made, it should go a mile high. Why not? We're counting
you in. I've told the princess all about you. You taught me everything, Uncle Ernest, you made me what I am today. I owe it all
to you. We got the message, didn't we, Princess? I'm to be Jesus.
Somebody has to be the crystal diode." He tapped his head. "It
may as well be me. I'm chosen. That's what it's all about. I've got
to build the most powerful mothering station on the *globe*—the
globe, d'ya hear?—and send out the Word. I don't have the plans
with me, but I been studying the Roslyn radio station's antenna
for weeks. Sitting under it. The time has come. Her brother's got
the money. Hasn't Rudolph got the money, Princess?"

She nodded, babyish, sucking her lips.

"We're cutting you in. You got the kind of ideas we need.
And Princess Ruby—what a head! Princess, pick up Jupiter. Show
Uncle Ernest what your head can do."

She shook her body violently.

"She's got an even greater head than mine. Come on, Princess, Jupiter shouldn't be hard."

"You're embarrassing her. I've, uh, settled down, Arnold!"

"Oh, man, you've let that A. A. knock the wind right outta
you. I could tell, snap, like that, when you answered the phone.
You sounded dead. I've got to raise you, Uncle Ernest. The
baroque still lives! The truly imaginative man is still free. All
that's needed, in my case, is a little fancy footwork in the financ-
ing. Some plane fares. You don't happen to have two thousand
you might sink into our station? Oh, Christ, we were *depending*
on you." He sighed vastly. "Wow, man, what A. A. has DONE to

you."

He slouched back—an arm thrown over his skull, pinpoint eyes farsighted with fantasy, the overhead hand twisting and splaying his plans, index finger lecturing.

"How I remember you in your glory! Those tremendous *vibes*, an intellectual Zorba the Greek—'The ionized golden solar horses dripping flame through my livingroom, splattering pollen slag like Bethlehem Steel in the night!' Oh, man. How can you be deaf to these things? This is the man you were. I want to raise him! That's my job, Uncle Ernest. I raise the dead. Don't you want that man alive again?"

"May every angel in heaven protect me from him, Arnold."

He looked about wideeyed. "We're being bugged. Who lives over there?"

"I don't know. There's a couple of brick walls between us."

"I can hear 'em talking. I have very sensitive ears, haven't I, Princess? I've had to develop my hearing. She picks up Saudi Arabia every night and relays it to me and I break down the message. The whole process takes hours, sheets and sheets of code." He glared at the bugged wall. "I'll get that fucker. I'll jam him to shit."

He squealed his tenor at the wall for a half hour, relentlessly, a forty-ton tractor trailer skidding an endless mountain curve. I shrank.

"That was a good workout. We better cut out, Princess. Don't say a word until we're on the street. I'll keep in touch, Uncle Ernest. I hope to hell something shakes you outta this coldness."

When they were gone, I sat thanking God for not striking me a second time with Arnold's demons.

Chapter Twelve

A Chinese red and charcoal material sprang richly before me as I closed my eyes—beamed in, so vivid, a direct impression of some woven pattern. I couldn't figure out its meaning. It's very clearness was a sign, a signature that I *could* see a picture more intense than a dream.

Then I stood in the unintelligible murk of a barroom, by a fullbodied redhead in a Chinese red and charcoal dress. Somebody I knew, but her name escaped me. She moved against my knee, her leg touching my inner leg. My bloodstream turned to seltzer, a prickling sex urge. Her green eyes sank into me, a soft glow joining our outlines, and she asked, "Well, what are we going to *do-o*?" Oh, I didn't *know* what we were going to do, but my matter felt electric.

Just before I met Irene, I'd spent a half year taking off sixty pounds, shaved off a beard untrimmed in seven years, and had a waist-length ponytail amputated. Almost at once, a hysteric quality went out of my voice and my normal tenor relaxed into near baritone. Friends did not recognize me until I said who I was, then still didn't believe it. I'd changed, inside and out. And my romantic life turned inside out also. When I met Irene, I'd been sober three years and a souped up, illusionary light had been drained from my eyes.

The loveliest A. A. I knew began kissing me with great heart whenever we met at my regular meeting. At last, just after I moved in with Irene, this young thing took me aside following a meeting and stood staring at me, waiting. A redhead, she wore a Chinese-cut red and charcoal print, its figured shades drawing me into a half-world of sylphs and shadowy undergrowth. She seemed in two worlds at once but I sensed real breasts breathing at me under her Chinese starlight.

"Well," she said, "aren't we going to?"

"To what?"

"You know. I'm ready. I've been waiting for you to ask."

"*Ohhh!*" I said. "Oh, I see. Well! *Uhhh*, I, uh, it's, uh, *TOO LATE!* I just moved in with somebody."

"Oh. Well." She winked. "I'm not the sort to come between people."

I said nothing, sighing.

"Maybe later," she said, undimmed.

"I'm sorry. Boy, I really am sorry."

That night she wavered before me, more vivid than the hand I write this with, her eyes brookwater, her face over-alive with fellow-feeling for me. At last! How I'd longed to touch her. We move together. Bliss bursts in hovering silver bits, a rich mist. Her fine-grained light merges with my being. Unbearable sympathy binds us.

At our next meeting she walked up to me, smiling with a frank, brilliant knowingness, a naked gaze that confirmed our love act in the astral. She nodded. I nodded. Our solar beings lifted remembering the ideal merger, and after this slaking exchange she walked silently away. Again I sensed two worlds about her, a figure hidden within hers, some memory of breasts rising to grip the present.

Psychic events happened daily in our lives until we began accepting them as normal. I saw Irene freshly—sensing, glimpsing, knowing the spirit within only lent her greater carnal impact on my eye, a bright mingling of spirit at risk in flesh. When we first made love, she saw a great burning diamond, which remained for many nights.

I got double-vision (sober) at my regular A. A. meeting. The members around our table were spiritual beings with spiritual problems they thought were earthproblems. The very room doubled, until I knew—strongly—that this meeting was taking place in heaven, which was located in the very chairs and bodies we sat in, a softly leaping glow binding us, using us for its channel. And then I knew that this meeting, this very meeting, was being attended by spirits, a crowd of recovering spirits—astral drunks—who were at the only place in the universe where they could get sober-minded and the serenity that really leads somewhere. And some "dead" friends in the fellowship were there too, not in token memory, but really, really there. And sometimes they'd let me know, in a rush of feeling, when it was my turn to speak: they stood around and helped, especially if asked.

I began trusting Irene's intuition as strongly as my own. My intuitions connect like base hits, hers are more subtle, a feeling-sense that radiates and seeks and *knows*. When we met, she stayed dizzy for two days, feeling my feelings shooting at her through the brick length of Manhattan from the Bronx. When she wanted her daughter, away for summer courses in Idaho, to call her, she walked out into our roofgarden tomatoes and willow tree, closed her eyes and said, "Laura, phone me!" Within five to fifteen minutes, the calls came. I began getting tweezes from my mother's ulcer, and would think SWEET COLD CHOCOLATE MILKSHAKE, and the tweeze went away. I phoned her down in Florida, she said that at that moment she was eating chocolate ice cream for her ulcer, I told her to forget real ice cream and just use her mind. One Friday when we had a two o'clock pickup at a car-rental agency some blocks from the Strand Book Store, Irene took a cab with a girl friend to the Strand (the friend was getting out there) and arrived exactly at two o'clock as I walked out the Strand's front door, late, and found her smiling in the cab parked before me. We were supposed to have met blocks away at that very moment. Five seconds either way and we would not have met. Why had the friend been prompted to go to the Strand? There are eight million other people in New York, any one of whom conceivably could have walked out that door in that five seconds. These events began happening and happening.

I was gifted with a dream about the death of Jung. We were sitting in wicker chairs, under a poplar, in his garden. He was very old, kindly, and massively fragile, and a cloud of infinitesimal, spermlike lights popped and vanished about his wide-brimmed panama. I was amazed to be sitting with this master of staggering insights and zealous struggle with the unknown. A long cobra glided out of the marigolds, freezing me. I couldn't speak. The old man spoke earnestly to me, a sudden waterglitter bursting from his glasses as he laughed and pointed his pipe, saying, "Called or not called, God is present." And he waved his pipe over the umbrella table. A spot appeared in the air and grew into a television set before us. The great cobra, large as a python, had wrapped him, its head slowly working his hat over his eyes. I was stoned but he was not at all worried as his hat fell to the ground and the snake rested its head on his. The set came on and on the tube Jung was conducting me through his library. Here were more psychic and alchemical texts than anyone could read in a lifetime, centuries of psychic experience. He was telling me about spirit-communication happenings in his life that ruled out mere telepathy and that he felt were confirmed occurrences. The Jung on TV told me how his unconscious had broken through with several precognitive experiences and seen the earth in glorious blue light once when he had nearly died of illness and gone out of his body to soar a thousand miles above the planet. I noted that he was even richer to hear than read. Now the tube had us into a hospital where psychic investigators sat about watching "dead" relatives appear out of nowhere to guide the dying to a new plane. The dying opened their eyes as if gazing at some shining Matterhorn. Jung talked on to me, saying, "Thought has measurable force and can radio a cheerful blessing or encouragement just where it's needed, in this world or the next, my boy, as quickly as you could speak it were the person standing before you. We impress ourselves on distant people constantly, though the thought may be held in abeyance by them until they are receptive. At this moment, several of my friends around the world are dreaming of my own death. You see, I am about to die." Then he smiled gaily and said, "Nonetheless, I don't want to go!" And his fist clenched. Suddenly the air darkened and heavy drops struck the table umbrella. Jung smiled shyly in his chair. A glass dropped from his fingers. He looked idiotically happy as a wobbling bright globe rose over his head. I felt unhinged. The ground quaked beneath me and a fissure burst the garden. With a crash, a giant lightning bolt split the poplar tree, and I knew he was dead. He was drooling.

I found a record for self-hypnosis on my shelf—I'd bought it ten years ago to help me stop drinking. I followed its instructions in the quiet of my bedroom and began going under, hoping to find my spirit guide. Down I went, and after a while blissful feelings surged up and down me. At last, a vision appeared, so bright I was stunned. It was my own head in a silver helmet against a half-clouded, fiery salmon sun. Apparently my guide was to be Mercury.

Each night as I fell asleep tattered colors and unbidden swimming forms raced through my eyeballs—sheets and pieces of light Hindus call *vritti*— I used to see them on pot and LSD (no more, thank God). If I woke in the middle of the night to go to the bathroom, the little light picked up from streetlamps charged these *vritti* until my brain swirled pleasantly, seeing through the veil into the lower desire-level of the astral. One glance at a soft shaft breaking into the livingroom would set off a geyser. But something must have happened, perhaps I grew, since these witless pleasures never occur anymore.

One Sunday morning I met another sexy A. A. on the street.

She'd been a hippo hippie wino but had sobered up and slimmed into a powerfully attractive girl with a soft sandy smile and green-blue eyes. I kept an intense straight face but my desire ran red under her needle-spray glow as she lighted up over the book I carried. She revealed she'd been a Spiritualist for many years. Through meditation she'd developed a healing power which took the shape of a bright globe she could project to an ill person miles away—the ball of energy would travel up the body and bring quick recovery. Several of her friends, and my friend her fiancé, had seen this ball appear when they were sick and found it entering their feet and going out their heads. It almost never happened by her willing it. She only needed to send feelings of comfort and the ball did the rest. Her fiancé had been helped this way, then phoned to ask her, "Were you just 'balling' me?" He too was a Spiritualist and had out-of-body trips. One night he found himself halfway across the country, watching his five-year-old nephew piss in a potted plant at midnight. The boy looked up and saw his uncle watching. Next morning he asked his mother when his uncle had arrived, and why didn't he come down for breakfast? That morning the fiancé, piqued by his trip, phoned his sister and told her that her son was killing the plant on the landing. She told him the boy had seen him the night before. I too was piqued by this and took Irene to a Spiritual Science Mother Church meeting in a little room in Carnegie Hall. We were disappointed by an elderly lady minister who repeatedly insinuated that a male and female avatar had been parked in a UFO over Yugoslavia for six months and in a few weeks were moving on to Miami. We were given nothing but her toweringly sincere assurances for this. When I told my Spiritualist friends about this visit, they laughed but vouched for their own meetings in Old Greenwich. The four of us began having regular Thursday night dinner and meditation. A current of affection bound us. One night I had a rather greasy sex-dream of her, in a green-blue glow, but once again the girl in my dream had a certain charge that leaped from the past. Somewhere, an unspent force was seeking me out.

We went to the rival Spiritual Regeneration Movement on West Forty-Sixth for a healing service. The smallest church in the world, a tiny shoebox with eight or ten massively carven pews and a lectern-desk. A dark young man gave a nervous sermon and answered questions we'd written and folded up. He was very enthusiastic and vague. Then Irene and I stood with our eyes closed while two ministers, another young man and a shy little round woman built like an elf, cleaned the scum off our auras by waving their hands about us and throwing the scum to one side. My head felt dipped in lemon juice, my cheeks shrank tight, my lips shriveled and writhed. Frankly, I was imitating Durwood going into trance. Irene was trembling but fearless. The man polished her with surprising athleticism, we thought, but the little lady working on me coughed repeatedly over my tobacco-brown magnetic body. She had shockingly violet pupils whose black centers widened, transmitting twilight. My Mercury burst into my vision, burning more intensely than ever before. She excused herself to wash her hands, then returned to clean and cough some more, saying that I needed more work and should see the athlete for further restoring. After the meeting the minister who'd led the service said this was the greatest healing he'd ever attended. He shone with exhaustion. Perhaps we'd all needed it. We were happy. During the service the sound system (we thought) carried a supernatural rapturous violin that dipped and soared through ghostly quarter-tones and glissing minors—later we turned to find another little old lady fiddling with closed eyes and mouth beaming.

We felt restored and *up* all week. Just by suggestion, perhaps.

We went to the Rudolph Steiner Anthroposophical Society for a service—I'd read his autobiography but found his other books pompously Germanic and dense. The lecture was so abstract that fatigue closed in with its rubber jaws. I wanted to tape my eyes open. The very air was gummy. Afterward, a magnificent fiddler soared through Bach's *Third Unaccompanied Sonata*, a fantastically difficult work. Steiner himself was sending down vibes of uplift.

Then came the day that glorious old C. W. Leadbeater himself came visiting from India and was allowed to speak at Theosophy Hall. His status was very complicated. The most venerated Theosophist alive, he was also Bishop of the Liberal Catholic Church of Australia, a Jansenist sect which claimed true apostolic succession—it broke from Catholicism over papal infallibility. But the Theosophists too had split into rival lodges. One kept strictly to Madame Blavatsky as revealed, rather haywiredly, in *The Secret Doctrine*, and the other accepted the Buddhic notions of Annie Besant and Leadbeater, a pair of astral travelers whose clairvoyant messages from Master Kuthumi and his rarified companions (who descended from planes above planes above planes) burst more bindings than the endless letters of Madame Blavatsky herself.

Rather stirred, we met his ship at the Forty-Third Street pier. Snowwhite mane flowing, a great blue-jewelled cross bouncing and blazing on his green shirt, he swept onto the wharf like a lion, tossing his purple cloak and hopping about as if roaring for a High Mass or many-layered, long Latin ceremony to munch like a napoleon. His brilliant opalescent eyes danced over his attendant corps of teenage Indian disciples, all boys. He cooed left and right at the great stone incarnation of Manhattan as if it were real and not a passing coconut grove on the physical plane, and was soon whisked into a tiny red Volkswagen with limousine grill and driven off to Theosophy Hall.

Fittingly, he led a vesper service that evening. We walked over Seventy-Second Street, a yellow star over the green sunset, and into the brick hall. Banked with purple dahlias, hydrangeas and lilacs, the lavenderscented meetingroom was a flood of astral hues, packed and electric. We sat in a hush of energy. At last Leadbeater appeared, clearing his throat, in a purple robe scrawled with apricot figures. The hall burst into silence, lifting to a higher vibration. Our minds faded into a long Indian twilight where still windless plane trees spread hammered branches. His bodiless milky eyes looked out at the hedge of little old ladies nodding and smiling in the front rows, his frank skull balanced on very long yellow eye-teeth.

"Hullo," he said. And tamped his glistening chin with a wrist.

The front rows suddenly nodded like goldenrod.

"The Lord Maitreya conveys His greetings to you through my Master Kuthumi and the Master Morya, whom I visited last night." He sighed, then breathed deeply, a fire rising in his marvelously mellow voice. "And I bring greetings from HPB, who was there also and desires that all our lodges band into a united and glorious energy in service to our Lord Maitreya. Madame Blavatsky is quite distressed, but hopeful that we can knock down our fences. And I am hopeful. There is nothing we can not do or dare."

Again he looked at the little old ladies and seemed to think twice. "I haven't much to say about cosmogenesis, theogony or anthropogenesis this evening. That will have to wait until our receivers are better tuned. However, we all believe in much the same things. Or I think we do. We believe in the magnetic health of the etheric body and that it dies with the physical vehicle. We believe in the astral soul or framework which produces the etheric and physical vehicles and survives death. We believe in that imageless power of the mental body that produces the astral being. We believe in that great causal Will which guides the mental form. And we believe in the solar nucleus of the Self or that great dynamo producing the vibratory planes. We believe in these things. They are attested to by a vast body of astral travel and investigation. Our business is plain. We must guide spirits out of the desire-hobbled lower astral and confusions of the physical. Only then are we free to set our souls on the path to final deliverance into the heart of Lord Maitreya Himself. We believe these things. I take it for granted that we have not a doubt in the world about any of these things." The corners of his mouth were streaming wet.

Bishop Leadbeater spoke on, growing ever more merry, and twinkled through high abstractions and the Buddhic plane for two hours and forty-five minutes. Despite a blackboard aid, he failed to lift us from the astral coalmines. Fatigue gummed us, our heads heavy as concrete. There was no violin. He drooled in the beyond.

But we'd put much work into his books and were not ready to give up. I told my elderly analyst (he's been writing his own book, *Metabiology*, for thirty years) that all this study had killed my streetside erotomania, or response to bra-less young persons on the paving. I must have forgotten those dreams. I told him I focus my lovelife entirely on Irene, if I'm not bedeviled by deadlines and other anxieties that whack me out of focus.

"The closer I get to a state beyond those red flashes, whims and moods of unfocused desire, the more keenly they grip me, Doctor. My eye peripherally victimizes me with habit-glimpses at the uncupped nipple, the lip-shaped crease in pants—not to be poetic, Doctor—and buttocks, buttocks, buttocks, a relentless pressure of street sex to which I have no response, no fantasy— only unstoppable *eyeballing*."

"I see."

"It's a kind of anesthesia of the testicles when I'm outdoors."

"My boy, you've gone too far."

And so it came as a great relief when we went to stay for a long weekend at Irene's country house on the Cape, where I could sit on the four-wheeled lawnmower for eight hours and mow, mow, mow in complete control of myself. What joy! What refreshment!

One weekend we drove up with her reading Leadbeater's *Man Visible and Invisible* to me all the way. A cloudburst drove cars off the road. We crept along in our watertight box, the rain so heavy I could barely see a tail-light ahead. Irene read aloud by flashlight. I got lost. Then the car went dead and I glided off the road. We'd been so abstracted by Leadbeater we'd not bought gas since leaving New York. I got out in the downpour to flag a car to some midnight gas station in the rain plane.

"You can't leave me here!" Irene cried.

"Then come with me." I was not angry.

"I'm afraid to get into a strange car. That's my worst nightmare!"

I stood torn in the deluge.

Irene dropped her face into her hands and prayed. "*Please send the Marion police!*" She opened her eyes and saw four glowing blue bulbs backing into our car with a chain dangling from a winch. It was the tow-truck which the police would have had to call—a step beyond her prayer. She shivered, the prayer answered so fast and richly that she was unnerved for hours.

That night we slept upstairs and hardly had I begun falling asleep when I rolled through the bed, the floor, and bounced wide awake against the ceiling below our floor, in a shiningly clear, see-through house. Our house, the one I was supposedly sleeping in. I was not asleep. I was looking up through the bedroom floor and through the bathroom wall at the bathroom. It was evenly lighted everywhere, every corner and beam a clear blue, from an even light outdoors. I saw through the porcelain sink,

the shelves, the shower curtains, and the whole toilet works—
it was there out of mental habit. I sensed the immensity of the
tremendous blue world beyond the walls. The light was a light I
could live with for a very long time. Then I looked out a corner
of the bathroom window. There were no hills. The Atlantic was
flat, curveless, nearly clear as air, and level as far as I could see. It
seemed to rise beyond.

I felt fear, blacked out, woke up instantly, and lay bathed and
clean for one clear moment of absolute gratitude.

PART THREE

PART THREE

Chapter Thirteen

Gowned, she sat in a garden with her back to me, an arm swanned along the backrest.

Clairvoyant cornflowers shone in shadow, blue shades dying on the air. My eye swam about the garden. Goldenrod darker than goldenrod, egg-yolk yellow. Light rippled in a fast brook-waver. Each bloom had a second image, not the blur of a shaken photograph but a slight doubling that gave sharper focus and color a stereoptical richness. Color as solid as chalk shot through each flower. Everything was spellbound, firm but shallow. My curved sight passed through each growth, doubling stems and sprays into two fused gardens.

Blooms took up more space than I had ever sensed. I'd never seen the astral as it is, only with everyday sight. Neither dreams nor acid had brought me material color, nor granted such enriched roving intensity. Never had being been so fulfilling and God-created.

Her pink white arm emerged from the shoulder and lay along the white wicker. Here at last was true flesh, not a mere body pallor or facing of skin but pink-shot flesh. I saw her whole head at once, the hair, the face that would not yield its name, the rounded head withholding the full power of its glance. Perhaps she knew I would melt into wakefulness. Foolishly, I forced my eyes to her hand, instead of moving my mind, and eye-pressure instantly dimmed the air. I'd begun to seek rather than accept, act rather than be. I simply might better have thought, Who are you? The garden would have held its jell, and she would have turned. Could I have braved her eyes in that beautiful strong garden?

Silver rain leaped steadily from a street . . .
Rain falling at a Canal Street subway exit, my eye at street-level, the late afternoon a gray glow.

We sat at a lecture on spiritual healing. My head drooped, and then the worrying hard melancholy of rain was *there* so vividly that I knew I had seen something that was happening at that moment.

"It's raining on Canal Street," I told Irene, when we left the hall.

As Roberta Winters had foreseen, at my reading months earlier, Irene and I were at the three-day Spiritual Frontiers Fellowship psychic convention on Staten Island—and surrounded by every known manner of psychic. Nearly four hundred of them! On the first day the psychics had looked as if they'd just wandered in from a trailer park. We were the only lovers on the Wagner College campus. After round-the-clock lectures, personal life readings, bloody films of psychic surgeons (some made real cuts and some were dazzling frauds), healing vibrations, a trance dance, past-life recall as a diagnostic tool, dream analysis, healing with metals, gems and colors, and a lecture on William James in the afterlife, it all warmed up like a big, gladhanded A. A. shindig.

The gray rain picture—it felt *shoved* into my head. No link to anything arose. Solemn and happy, I sensed some spurt of true clairvoyance having been granted me. But why rain on Canal Street?

I picked up a green acorn from the grass and thumbed its smoothness. Its brown cap and full shape impressed me with Cynara's boyish cheeks at fourteen. Her eyes had a Chinese twinkle.

These bits of clearsight were coming daily and nightly. They were not spiritual gifts but a growing natural awareness that arose from acceptance, pictures from a deep silence. Irene had been aware of solar stomach energy sinking and rising in waves for over a month. At the convention she had at last been to Roberta Winters for a reading—she'd been told that her mother was *still* around but more silent. This was a relief, since Irene had a foreboding that her mother was reincarnated into her daughter Laura, born nine years after the mother's transition. Mother had a message: "Irene, be patient and wait."

"What did that mean?" I asked.

"I think she meant about higher consciousness."

We turned off the light in our dorm room. Falling asleep, I was shaken suddenly A rather stupid-faced startled man was looking at me down a hole. He was about four feet above me. "Are you ready to come out yet?" he asked. I woke at once. His loutishness surprised me. But I'd built up a sense of happy peril.

In this budding new world, I needed a strong spirit of active fellowship, an openheartedness toward the beings I'd meet there. I might be there a very long time someday! Any hint of superiority or distaste could be read instantly. You are stark naked emotionally on the astral, every passing thought or desire unhideable. You can not withhold good will.

I closed my eyes. *POP!* Two women sat on a couch watching me. "That guy makes horrible faces," one said (I must have been imitating Durwood again) *Fear!* I whisked awake. It'd been a ratty couch, the women unpleasantly fat. Getting that way myself. I blessed them, then prayed, "Lord, let me do good works in my sleep." At once, a small sporey purple light spiraled into sight, coming toward me with a soft swirling chalky tail, and grew larger, a strange rich refreshment spilling down my spine and body. My sight grew wall-to-wall purple, not a trace of imagery, only clear purple light I could see into and which filled my cells until I felt entirely reborn as a clear twilight material. I was afraid to move my eyes. Then, unstoppably they crossed and rolled upward, as if to see into high heaven, and the far deeps of indigo faded. I could not bring them back.

Irene woke up sighing. She'd dreamed of a dim white horse galloping silently up Sixth Avenue past Jefferson Market and that my elderly doctor had written her a mash note declaring his love, which upset her deeply.

"Then you rushed out into the street and sat down. I came out and sat beside you. I felt that because of your old feelings for Cynara, there was no help for us. Some damage had happened to us that was beyond repair. I said I'd be your stoic friend but you were distracted to tears. I'd never seen you like that. I was devastated."

A grand old woman with emerald eyes looked down my hole. "Spuhlendid! Can you *r-r-r*ead in the dark?" she trilled. "Use your fingers and the book will appear. You *can r-r-r*ead with your fingers, you know. Every alive book has a heartbeat in it—its superconscious atomic weight and healing vib*r*-rations. Solar vib*r*-rations. You're an Aries, aren't you?"

"Not astrology!" I cried in my sleep. "Not that drugstore shlock! I drew the line at reincarnation and Edgar Cayce, but I got sucked in. Now astrology!"

In the "Afterlife of President Kennedy" lecture that day, Judy Jones declared that all the transitioned Kennedys deny reincarnation while asserting the great danger of possession by lower astrals, an act sometimes passing for reincarnation. Her *Afterlife of President Kennedy* was just out.

I held up my hand. "We have three books dictated by William James to Jane Revere Burke and he also stresses possession over reincarnation."

"That's right," Judy Jones thumped.

Irene added, "And in Dr. Carl Wickland's *Thirty Years Among the Dead*, the doctor's wife brings in the spirit of Madame Blavatsky and she renounces her own theories on reincarnation."

"*Right!*" Judy's blue eyes burst her glasses.

"What I want to know," I said, "is why Arthur Ford, the founder of Spiritual Frontiers Fellowship, espoused reincarnation in *The Life Beyond Death* and then dictated a great deal more confirming it to Margery Marchbanks in *A Kennedy Beyond* after Arthur'd transitioned."

Judy clamped her new book oath-takingly. "If you read *The Life Beyond Death* carefully, you'll see that he does *not* come out for reincarnation. In fact, he's very cautious not to. He simply *wavers!* As for *A Kennedy Beyond*, well, perhaps Margery is a little incautious. I've talked with Arthur often—in fact, *just last week!*—and he denied vehemently that he'd ever said such a thing to Margery."

The world's fattest Fat Man in a Blue Suit pulled his chair right in front of Judy and cut in repeatedly. Finally he asked, "May I sit in your chair? I know all about this Kennedy reincarnation stuff."

"Later."

He steamed on. "Lemme check you out on Kennedy's afterlife. I know all about it."

"After class."

He was the most difficult being to love all weekend. I never made it. At one famous healer's class, he broke in endlessly. His last question was, "Can you heal yourself? How can anyone believe in you if you can't do that? Do you agree or don't you?"

The grand old lady healer smiled. "He who has himself for a patient has a fool for a doctor."

I felt triumph. Unfortunately.

Chapter Fourteen

The twinkling blueblack velvet of lovarkite, a mineral that pol-
ishes to a clear face with flecks below, shimmers like two worlds
in one—it's praised for heightening clairvoyance. I'd seen a piece
and had to have my own.

On my way to the Astra Gallery of Minerals, I wondered,
Am I after an idol?

I stopped before a delicatessen where I'd twice slipped up
on eight-ounce Caramello bars. Lord, I began, and my Helpers,
please . . . I couldn't finish the prayer for a shield against Caramello bars. It would take away my sweet test of will! But I mumbled the prayer, grudgingly.

That evening our phone rang as Irene served a great platter
of fried eggplant. It was John L., an A. A. friend with eighteen
months perfect abstinence in Overeaters Anonymous. He was
calling out of the blue to offer his services should I want to go
back on my O. A. food plan. His open gentle timbre moved me,
despite myself.

"Gee, John, I'm not having any problems. I mean guilt problems. I'm just eating *reasonably*. No problems! I, uh, it's only that,
uh, well, I'll tell you, I just got back from a three-day weekend at

a Spiritualists convention and am feeling very *spiritual*. Reasonable and, uh, spiritual."

"That's good. I've been a Spiritualist for fifteen years. And a very accurate medium. I was just thinking of you and thought you might need a call. You're just sitting down to supper?"

"Well, yes. You're a psychic?"

"A very accurate one. They wanted me to be ordained but I was still drinking then. When I meditated it got so I was only pulling in lower astrals. So I stopped meditating. I stopped everything. Anyway, I just got a flash about you, a smell like fried olive oil."

"I see." I feinted him into the hen fight on reincarnation between Judy Jones and Margery Marchbanks.

"I was supposed to meet Arthur Ford the night after he died," John said. "We were having study class. So we pulled in Arthur the night after he died and *he* led the class for the entire period. It was the greatest psychic experience of my life. He was great! He was a terrific pal of Bill Wilson's, who saved his life once. Arthur'd had a heart attack and passed out on his floor. Bill was passing by several blocks away when one of Arthur's Helpers tuned in and directed him straight to the apartment, though Bill was on an important errand. He just went straight in the door and found him gasping on the rug."

"Bill W. never said *he* was psychic, did he?"

"Only about booze." Bill W. cofounded A. A.

"Did Arthur settle the reincarnation problem when you pulled him in?"

"All he talked about was drug addicts and drunks in the

lower astral and how he was going to devote all his time to helping them. I didn't know he was talking about me, of course."

"Do *you* believe in reincarnation, John?" I whispered. "It's become a rather meaningful issue around our house."

"Oh, I always have. I had memories of earlier lives as a child. I was shocked when my religion—I was Jewish—didn't include it. I found out later that it once did. So did Christianity until the Council at Nicea. Now it doesn't matter. What counts is a life of love and service, one day at a time, don't you think? God is *always* Now, whether you're reincarnated or in the astral or here or wherethehellever you are. Right? God will always be Now."

"Boy, that's right." Why hadn't I thought of that?

I hung up, thinking about my mumble for help against the Caramello combine. One of my Helpers must have taken me seriously, and impressed me on John. A red signal alert on the Detect-O-Smell.

Irene sat waiting at table, sunk into Mary Lutyen's life of Krishnamurti. He'd been raised by Leadbeater and Annie Besant to be the new Messiah.

"My God!" she cried. "This is mind-boggling! Krishnamurti has QUIT the Theosophists! He dissolved all connections with the Society at thirty-seven." She lurched in her chair.

"Ungrateful whelp. Does he toss out reincarnation?"

"Shh! I don't know yet."

I stared at my eggplant cutlets, the bright tomato salad, fat steamed asparagus tips and—after kissing Irene's knee, wrist and arm—blessed the food and invisible ivy twining the table. The table shone.

Chapter Fifteen

Our Cape house has steep ladder steps to the bedroom and as I came down in darkness to let in the cat, a strong presence filled the dark and froze me to the ladder. Did Leadbeater know I was writing about him? His fangs are hard to forget, and I sensed him feeding nightly on the auras of his little boys.

I went to see my elderly doctor, hard at work on his three-volume *Metabiology*, and told him about Leadbeater.

"You know I knew him ?" he asked.

The room tilted. "*Leadbeater?*"

"Oh yes. He came to Nashville in 1914 and tried to get me to be the vehicle of the Messiah. Wanted me to give up my life and go to India as his star pupil. He said I had the aura he'd been searching for for thirty years. He wanted to prepare me for Initiation. He was going to awaken my clairvoyance, teach me astral travel, solar mechanics and so forth and conduct me to his two Masters in Tibet, a pair of materialized beings from the Buddhic plane or some such place who were the founders of the Great White Brotherhood. He already had that Hindu boy under his wing, the whole world knew about that."

"Krishnamurti?"

"That's him! We'd have been rivals for the vehicle. I thought Leadbeater was some sort of hypnotist. Very imposing, with strange eyes and a beard like Bernard Shaw's. He talked and talked with me—but I found him obnoxious. This was sixty-one years ago, sir! I was seventeen. 'I'm only a poor *human being!*' I told him. Actually, I was too psychic already—nearly psychotic—I'd never have survived. Being a Semite saved me from insanity. And now, doctor, *tell me your dreams!*"

"I'm stunned. What are your views on reincarnation?"

"It's something like that—*not* reincarnation, but something like that. It's more metabiological. Your dreams, sir!"

Doctor H.'s body is a fragile veil for limitless spiritual presence and mental strength. He is a geopolitical cosmic recluse whose eye tests the pressures in the tiniest countries and enclaves and follows each perilous gene shift among the races. For him, God is the hormic, experiencing, impulse-driven sperm that uses man for a taxi and is itself a taxi for a Wind or Word come down from timelessness in quest of Self. He is a divine cannibal who eats His own child as it feeds on Him. Hopefully, the old lion will soon explain all this much better himself. I'm truly eager to read it.

"I've been having astral fragments, Doctor. They're more vivid than dreams."

"At what point do they happen?"

"Mainly between waking and sleeping. I try to go to sleep with a blank screen while remaining wide awake. I go under with a clear mind. Last night—incredible! First I saw a man helping a crippled woman to walk on tiptoe with his arm around her waist."

"Would you be so good and gracious, as is your wont, to tell me what you think of this experience?"

"1 think I was helping some earthbound astral get up to the next plane. She wasn't old, just crippled. I don't know who she was."

"I see. Go on."

"Then I had a flying dream. I wasn't sure I could get up there and soar each time I tried. I'd slowly lift off a few feet, then slowly rise with greater speed and control as if going into deep meditation. To fly I had to focus myself in a deep way, then I'd break loose and soar. It was much like biofeedback and trying to make an unbroken beep on the machine, a release in the depths.

"Then I had a dream in which I was trying to flag a cab for Irene. And this morning she told me she had a dream in which I was flagging a cab for her."

"My word! What do you make of that?"

I shrugged. "In her dream we drove off together in the rain. In mine I found myself upstairs alone in our hallway and somebody had left this little baby I could hold in my palm. Lying on the floor, the smallest, most perfectly formed little baby. And I sat down in the hall with it, and was holding and talking with it in my hand. It had just been born! A girl with perfectly formed mature eyes that had a Chinese twinkle. The more I talked with it the more I found it was much larger than I thought, a not full-grown woman. There was something wrong with her forehead. It was soft and discolored, like a deeply bruised apple. And she talked fairly well but she must have had aphasia or something—

she'd talk but then she had this damaged brow which interfered with her thinking. This dream eludes me, but her eyes were utterly familiar."

"That was all?"

"Oh there's more! Another baby dream. I was crossing a very high bridge leading a baby by the hand. Suddenly it got away from me and slipped under the railing and fell. I raced down to the riverbank to look for the body. I was resisting the horror and explaining to myself where the baby really was now and that it had felt no pain at transition. The bridge was from this world to the next, I'd say."

"Well! Any more?"

"Then I saw a four-dimensional bluewhite tree shimmering and flowing with a blizzard of stuff like blossoms."

"Four-dimensional?"

"That's the way it really is in the astral. Things have an extra richness, Doctor. Deeper coloring and vibrance. You see things in the round—in their wholeness. It's the difference between face and head—objects have *headness*. I saw *you* there, Doctor, and your head looked transparent and opaque at the same time. And you had a magnetic gentlemanly smile."

"My, my, my! But it was only a dream?"

"I'm only reporting, Doctor. But I think I really saw you there."

"I don't remember being there, old chap."

"I don't think I was making it up."

"I see. Well, is that the end?"

"No, no. Then my difficulties began. I heard a ghostly whistling of a song called 'Laura'—it's a sort of misty song, Doctor. Believe me, I hate cheap musical cues even in dreams, but I'm only reporting."

"What do you mean, 'cheap musical cues'?"

"Well, it's Irene's daughter's name but it's also one of the names of my girlfriend who shot herself."

Doctor H. sighed hard. "If only that girl had come to me when we made her appointment! I know I could have helped. I really feel badly about her. I'm sure she'd be alive."

"She had some legitimate fears, Doctor. Well, in this dream Irene and I were married! Living in her house on a hill in Cape Cod near the ocean. And listening to our Franz Lehár marzipan music. We were in the bedroom when I looked out and saw this tidal wave a mile off coming at us. Huge! Here we'd just gotten married and were going to be separated. I grabbed Irene just as the wave hit. Well, the house shook, the floor split open like a walnut, plaster fell everywhere—it was the Frisco quake—and water burst through the windows. But—the house stood up. I went outdoors. Some astral pranksters were setting up jokes to fool rescue parties. Then this frantic white cat ran into our house. I felt some awful disaster warning when I saw the cat. Then a beautiful, sexy darkhaired girl rowed up looking for her cat. I think the cat was her spirit. She was somebody I knew, or at least she knew me the way she looked at me. Well, Doctor, I mean she was sexy! I brought her into this dark area in the house, hoping Irene wouldn't see us, and kissed her. Against her will, I'll say that. Then I felt her up. I can't describe it. She had a fantastically beautiful bosom but there was something too soft about it in my hand. It was there and it wasn't there. And then—oh, I can't say it—"

"Go on, my boy. I'm not easily shocked."

"This—RIDICULOUS—banal sentence began repeating in my mind while that misty whistling went on. Doctor, to have background music come into your dreams is a demeaning experience."

"Oh? What was the sentence?"

"'They kissed like people who, despite themselves, know they are going to be lovers.'"

He wrote this down, then slowly looked through me. "Ahem, how did you feel about this situation?"

"*Torn*—and marvelously ready."

"Ready for what? I thought you were happily married. A newlywed bathed in Franz Lehár!"

"That's why I was torn. But such a sweet tearing. To be torn like that is to be really alive. Two true loves! In both of whom I'm to receive fulfillment—and it's *happening*."

"Who was this girl?"

"Oh, it was *her*. But there's more."

"My heavens. You had a full night."

"Well, this wasn't a dream, it really happened. Saturday morning. I finally got Irene to Roberta Winters for a reading."

"Where was this?"

"At the Spiritualists convention. I was supposed to have a reading too, but we were late, so only Irene got one. Bear with me, Doctor—we'd been sitting at a lecture when suddenly my head dropped and a supervivid picture came into my mind of rain on a Canal Street subway exit. I'd used this exit the day before when buying a tape-recorder for taping our readings. What's more, I took my brand new recorder directly to a radio repair shop to have it checked out—I wanted absolute assurance about this machine.

"So we went to Roberta Winters. I suspected something because I had a headache—and so did Irene! Well, I started the recorder for her reading, and told Roberta Winters that I really had only one question to ask her. Then I showed her a picture from my movie of Cynara in a white-feathered cap and holding a white cat. She almost screamed. She turned her head and pushed the picture away. *'She's been after me all day!'* she cried, and began choking and rocking and sighing. Her eyes *filled*, Doctor—*'OHHH! OHHH! OHHHH!'* She'd not had a chance to protect herself. Cynara was halfway inside her, I guess. Finally she got her breath and sighed, *'She's—she's all right now. She's very upset, come here very upset, she's so full of—so emotional!* She wanted to tell you about her gratitude for your waking her up. She thinks she's going to be better now. She desperately wants to thank you. *OHH! OHHHH!* Oh, that's all, that's all I can take. No more, I can't tell you more. Did you get that on tape? I'll bet you didn't. There was too much power in the room.'

"So then I knew that the depressed image of the rainy station by had been impressed on me by Cynara. She'd followed me down to Canal Street when I bought the machine. She'd impressed me into going to the radio repairman to make certain her message would get through. She'd impressed me with the rain which was her despair at our sitting too long at the lecture and being late to receive her in spirit from Roberta Winters.

"Later, Irene came up to our room with the recorder. She was glowing, Doctor. Her mother'd been pulled in. I rewound the reel—the machine had been working perfectly, I hope you gather?"

"Quite."

"But the tape was empty."

Chapter Sixteen

Tidal and unstoppable, the bosom bombardment grew. Some learning stage that would burst me before I got my brain back.

I seemed hellbent on eyeballing a nipple that promised eternal fulfillment. A power greater than myself bobbed in the summer heat. God was impressing me with His pity and love—in breast form. They were *all* God, teaching me the everywhereness and resistlessness of His sympathy. But how would Master Kuthumi respond at high noon in the Village when God zapped His red ray of desire over the tidal bobbing? I did not know that I was being impressed by a spell that had driven me through twelve adoring years of wordfluff, or that the bosom I sought was not alive.

Irene walked out among the tomato plants and willows of our roofgarden, her nightgown shotgreen in the full moon.

"Where *are* you?" This music tore me from my book. *Unhh.*

Out I went. The bare white moon riding through steam over the library clock tower.

"I adore you. I never want to be separated from you."

"Right. Maybe we won't be."

"Not *maybe!*" She stamped.

"Well . . ."

"No! Don't say that."

"I don't want to lose you," I said.

"We've gone through too much to think we'll be separated."

"That's how I feel."

"It's you and me over there."

"*Mmn.*"

The moon clouded, shadowing her.

We went to bed. Reading manuscripts, her face serious.

"Guess whom I had lunch with today." Her eyes expectant.

"Thomas Edison?"

"No! Ellen Brown, she's an agent at Random House. She knew you several years ago. This is fantastic. She's a true believer. She had a dematerialization experience about a year after her husband died. She's never told anyone about it. She was on a Lexington Avenue bus uptown with all her luggage, trying to get downtown to a crosstown bus to a bus at Port Authority, and found she had only ten minutes to get there. She was desperate to get out to Long Island and kept saying *I've got to make that bus!*"

"She's a pretty, browneyed girl? Always looks like she's looking at a sunrise?"

"Well, yes. Are you listening? Finally she looked at her watch and had an anxiety paroxysm. She was determined, she lighted up, and suddenly found herself in Port Authority boarding her Long Island bus. Luggage and all! Three minutes had passed on her watch. She hadn't the slightest idea how she'd made it. Except she knew she hadn't got there normally—that was impossible."

"Something clicked, huh? She vibrated up an octave. The

A. S. P. R. Newsletter reported on two yogis in India who can do this. And Durwood saw Harry Slater do it on a streetcorner in Buffalo."

"The mind *swims!* Everyone in the world does things they're not telling each other."

Someone was in the room. My heart pounded. Naked on the end of the bed, she turned to me, smiling shyly.

"We need a slogan like PSYCHICS, COME OUT! Or PSYCHICS, UNITE! What do you think? Darling, what's wrong? You're red!"

"*Tobacco!*" I croaked.

"I'll get you a drink of something. Hang on." She jumped up and ran downstairs.

I was, somehow, skeptical. I saw her. She smiled. Her eyes asked something wordless. I wondered, without thinking it in words, why she wasn't dressed. Spirits usually show up in favored clothes. I saw and disbelieved.

Her eyes! I'd been praying for and blessing her nightly before falling asleep, but wondered why I could never get her face clearly in mind. I often have difficulty imaging some few faces and hers was one. No work would bring it into focus at any of the ages I'd known her. Now she was all there, at about twenty, her eyes direct, quiet, amused and friendly. So friendly, and soft with loving thankfulness.

She was there or she wasn't, but our beings could at last speak our feelings. Hers were already plain, a gratitude she took great pains to say in her look, and the fun, I'd guess, of appearing at last to a living being open to a visit. I found it hard to keep her unseen headwound from my mind, and did my best to show thanks for the visit, more the gentle friend than old lover. But that wound was there, if only in memory.

"Are you better?" Irene asked, handing me the glass.

"Thanks."

"What are you reading?"

"About Whitman. You know we have five volumes of Whitman's parlor talk recorded by Horace Traubel? He was completely under Walt's spell most of his adult life. When he lay dying in 1919, he had a Colonel Cosgrave at his bedside. At three in the morning they noticed a wavery light in the room growing larger and larger. Then it became Whitman's face—he'd been dead twenty-seven years, but had been hanging around Traubel's deathbed off and on for a couple of days, telling him, 'Come on, come on!' Traubel's wife Anne and a Flora Denison saw Walt on the north veranda, and they saw a phantom white boat with two lights at each end in the moonlight on the lake shore. Flora was a psychic observer and wrote everything down immediately to keep from coloring the facts. Whitman came up to the bed in full materialization, wearing a tweed jacket and his floppy broad-brim. Both Traubel and the Colonel saw him. He stood there a full minute, Cosgrave says, smiling reassuringly and nodding twice at Traubel who—despite a paralyzed tongue—said, 'There is Walt!' Then Walt passed through the bed towards Cosgrave, touched the Colonel's hand, which was in his pocket, giving him a low electric charge, then smiled at Traubel again, and faded away. Traubel died in beatitude."

"Oh my God, that's beautiful."

"Two witnesses to each materialization."

I looked down the bed. She had not faded. She looked as if she were crying unseen tears (for herself or Traubel?).

Irene fell asleep. I set aside her glasses—or my extra pair, she'd twice lost her own—and turned out the light after a last look at her face. If she dreamed of this room, would she see Cynara?

I said the Lord's Prayer and blessed many people and sank into half-sleep without remembering to remind myself to record my dreams. This wasn't necessary since my first and only memory of that night will always be with me.

A roseflush shot up my blood and took my heart away. She had lain down on top of me. I saw a glowing rose that burst me with gratitude—her gratitude to me, and mine to her for this touch, deepest sympathy flowing to and fro between us.

Chapter Seventeen

I met a Black woman sitting by the iron fence of Grace Church on Lower Broadway. She wore a black hood, ragged sweaters, wadded string around her neck, and her bushy hair was filled with twigs and leafmeal. Something lively about her eyes as she sat eating ice cream with a blue-string bathmat over her knees stuck with me. Not yet totally stupified by my shelves of occult books, I was on my way to Weiser's for two more. After dying, F. W. H. Myers, a famous psychic investigator, had dictated a description of the afterlife which I wanted to compare with Leadbeater's upper planes. But the Black's voice bugged me.

Her face, eyes and inner light were Irene's! How would I feel if this were Irene, out of her mind, loaded with old string and leaves, talking to herself on a curb and ignored by passersby?

I started back to give her a dollar, saw how I was buying myself off, made a phone call to the Women's Shelter a few blocks below on Lafayette, then went back.

She looked up at me.

"Hi. Here's a dollar and a token."

"Eat this."

She held up her ice cream cup and a loaded spoon.

"I'm too fat already."

"Go on, eat it!"

"Please, no."

"*Eat it!*"

I ate the spoonful and instantly felt some kind of peril in my tongue.

"Thanks."

"Now go in there and pray for yourself."

"I've been praying."

"Go in there and pray! Then come back and sit down."

"Here, take this."

She pointed at her garbage bag. "Throw it in there."

"All right." I dropped the dollar and token into the garbage.

"You can't help a pregnant woman."

"There's a token if you want to go down to the Women's Shelter."

"I got a home! Right over there! See that new building? They won't lemme in!"

Her voice rasped, was friendly, then rasped, her eyes rolling and arms flying.

"I been sleepin' out here four days. Don't matter, I'm just skin, no flesh in it. I'm a bag!"

She turned and began talking as a man with some "construction workers" sitting beside her, in her mind. She was the boss and telling them where to start work and what to do. She was a man: "Din't we BUILD that building? Now they won't let us in!"

A Black caretaker for the church grounds went in the iron gate beside her.

"See that man? He's pregnant. They stole my ten dollars and made him pregnant."

She suddenly got mad at me and walked around the corner and stood there barefoot. I sat by the garbage, my mouth still smarting from the ice cream. Passing people stared at her. At last she came back and sat on her ice cream cup, pointing at store doorways across the street.

"I made that doorway and that one and that one and the basement where they won't let me live—slept in 'em all." Her voice changed to a man's. "Built it! Won' lemme in now!"

"When did you build it?"

She got mad again. "You the one who stole my ten dollars, you ought to know." A young Black in a low-cut dress walked past. "Hey, *you sick!* You need help!"

The woman stopped, narrow-eyed, leaned down at the other, saying nothing but perhaps ready to help. The madwoman got up and faced the churchyard. "I'm gonna *change* all this." She threw out her arms stiffly, knowing exactly what she was doing, and with a large magic gesture rebuilt the green churchyard into something new on the lower astral.

Then she got mad at me and walked off. I got up and walked to Washington Square. She'd been stone serious about revamping the churchyard out of elemental essence.

I sat in the park looking at the druggies and fuzzies and looselimbed musicians and loungers and sank into a vision of millions of bad-tempered bodiless beings prodding the unstable with unbidden thoughts, emotions, strangenesses and forebodings, gloomy moods, impatience, anger, snappishness, mad outbursts, sentimental swamps, uncontrollable spells and needs and mindwanderings. I looked through Myers' dictation from beyond. Beside me, a thin young man with broken veins on his nose, a dark skimpy beard and thick glasses, leaned over. "You believe in all that?"

"A lot of it."

"It's none of it true. Beginning to end, it's nonsense. What's the point of it anyway, even if it were true? So my mother speaks to me from the dead. What's she got to say that's so great? Or important. She used to sit in a dark room doing automatic writing when I was twelve. I didn't believe a word of it. I believe in rationalism, though of course that's only a formal mode of thought—I mean it's not real but it's the best we have. Maybe telekinesis, I might go along with just a bit of it if it were a scientifically controlled experiment."

His iceblue eyes rolled with spiritual panic. I tried to tell him about recent out-of-body lab work done with airtight controls. I was speaking Eskimo, I guess. He dismissed me.

"I read philosophy. Self-educated, can't stand controls or teachers. There isn't a single philosopher today who accepts Spiritualism or psychic phenomena—William James?—not dependable—the stuff's not worth thinking about. I go along with the critical-naturalists up at Columbia."

"How about the General Systems Theory they're formulating up there?"

"What's that?"

"It's a kind of metaphysics of biology."

"Metaphysics is a trap. You go in there and the ground sinks away."

I thought of the Black woman and the astral possessing her, then this fellow's surprise the next time he sees his mother. His head lay on the concrete chess table like a cabbage wrapped in spaghetti, eyes rolling at the astrals skimming their plastic plates.

"I'm the kind of guy, people tell me, when I walk into a room and they're hot about something, I'm a pail of icewater. You can use sub-atomic theory to show the instability of any subject."

"You believe in sub-atomic particles?"

"I *know!*"

"But they're unstable."

"You don't understand sub-atomic physics."

I rose. He gave me his hand, then told me about politics in Trenton, and New Jersey prices, public utilities, and complained that Rockefeller owned twenty per cent of the earth. I left. He was lonelier than the Black woman.

Home to work. A Spanish A. A. phoned to mope about his work confusion, his girl, his money, his apartment and his divorce. His voice was faint as an astral cry. I told him he did not have to feel so disembodied nor be a victim of his moods, whims, manias and compulsions, that he should get off his ass and answer phones at Intergroup, that if he wanted to be recharged he had to help others, and that when his spirit was alive with service he'd solve his problems one at a time, not all at once. He hung up to go downtown and answer phones. I felt better.

She walked into the livingroom, unbidden but welcome, smiling, shapely, still twenty, and sat facing me on red plush. She was erect and waiting. My desire-mind began shifting, remembering last night. In the middle of a dream, Irene had arisen and gone on a trip and her daughter Laura had slid under the sheets to be my companion. Astral morality doesn't exist! When I woke I refused even to tape the dream.

In a flash, Cynara was beside me on the couch, mischief in mind. I moved back into the corner, drawing up my legs. She smiled about at the fireplace, the big bookcases and many hundreds of records, and leaned back restfully, a gesture meant only for me. Her finger toyed with red velvet nap. Then something smooth glided over the balls of my fingers, like a cat pleading to be stroked, its skull nudging me. My throat went dry.

I nodded and smiled. Again I had to put her headwound out of mind.

You're gonna have to forgive yourself and get active over there, I told her.

Her smile altered not a shade.

You seem to be out of that dismal plane you were in. You must be growing. Your recovery's coming right along, huh?

Only mischief.

That was all self-punishment, I said. You're really getting in focus, huh, getting better? Right?

Something flowed off her that was pure desire. She willed it off in waves.

Someday, uh, sweetheart, I hope we'll be friends on the astral. I, uh, understand spirits have very powerfully charged, uh, feelings with each other. Boy, it's really good to see you up and about. Talking about the astral—on my mother's side, we're octogenarians. We really hit the high numbers. It's gonna be a long time before I'm over there, quite likely. Makes you wonder what husbands and wives do over there when one's still back here for twenty or thirty years. I mean whether you remarry over there the way we do, uh, over here. Seems a terrific place in your better areas.

Her visit did not move me to verse.

Irene came home late. We had salmon salad and went to bed.

That night I again blessed Cynara in the dark, and told her she was welcome to crash here as long as she needed. Irene turned her light on again and sat up with a William James dictation.

"I love William James, he's such a dear. My day went off in fifty-five orbits at once, that place is a *madhouse!* I mean the whole staff walks about half-insane with lost faces—like zombies in menopause. You and William James are my islands, darling. I'll feel sick if I don't read something sane. I'm worried."

"What about?" I dropped Stevenson's *Twenty Cases Suggestive of Reincarnation* heavily.

"What if there isn't reincarnation?"

"Then I'd write Stevenson a nasty letter."

"Seriously!"

"Well, I don't know. You want to wait for each other?"

Great pain filled her glasses. "What about *Egypt* and *Rome* and the Civil War together! How can you ask?"

"Just asking worries you? Honey, we're together, thick or thin."

She kissed me. "Promise?"

"Don't worry your pretty little ectoplasm. I used to believe

I'd survive in my works. What stupendous horseshit. Can you imagine yourself bound to some texts and doomed to hear your enthusiasms repeated for centuries? There's gotta be something better."

She switched off the wacky reading lamp—it went off, on, off. We kissed and I tried to focus on Irene.

As I sank into half-sleep, I blessed them both. I tried to see Cynara vividly, but she would not appear. At least she was no longer the drained, bedeviled mother of twenty-six I'd seen a few months before her suicide. Force away the headwound. Suddenly she touched me within, seven times in a minute (I counted), a flush lifting my breast and reddening every nerve in my being. I was grateful for this response to my blessing, which I had given with great energy and concentration. I felt the energized blessing zap outward. I really wanted to help.

I woke. The lamp was on. Irene was halfway through Stevenson, her face pale and driven. I felt guilt and that someday she would read our every thought this evening. Durwood and many others say the whole past is stored in some great vibratory library quite accessible on the next plane. Well, thoughts are vibes! If you want to see some famous event, it won't be too clear what's happening—there's no placard saying BATTLE OF HASTINGS—1066 A.D. You just see some mailed soldiers debarking at dawn and carrying spears. Just moving men, too particular for a big picture. Or there you were in bed, saying one thing, thinking another. The whole boring but honest record is out there, or in here, *tap tap*.

Chapter Eighteen

I sat down to bring in James Joyce on my electric typewriter.

First I asked my Helpers for a shield (no dead derelicts, please), then sat back with fingers poised, taking myself under. I went down like an elevator. Slowly, then more strongly, eyes closed, something came through in lower case without commas or periods—

joyce here opening his ponderous and marble jaws your works purpose is to glorify entertain and instruct what it is about you will know later do not worry about flimflam but do not compose in cold green purgatorial jellies rave softly on strive for the common touch i have always been most alive with porters streetcar conductors butchers who were all my friends the wake is quite popular over here and read like the daily mail where are blavatskys panties now theyre in the secret chambers of the golden dawn society where I draped them surely john mccormack is a deathless tenor hes here now were melodious boys all in pansonical colors erubescent farewell

I suspected it wasn't Joyce but some lying assistant professor or sub-sub- wino librarian out for a boost of red. I knew what he meant by green astral jellies—*stick to the facts.*

I'd seen her yesterday walking out of the kitchen, so I knew she was around. Maybe she was reading some of my occult books. Or reading me as I followed Krishnamurti—he was flying through the Buddhic plane with Leadbeater and Annie Besant to his Initiation among the Tibetan Masters. What piqued me was that Krishnamurti was still vigorous at eighty, as highly respected, literate, intelligent and inspired a spiritual leader as any alive, and that he was still attesting to these astral travels with the celebrated Theosophists sixty-five years ago—from whom he'd split thirty-eight years ago. If Cynara was reading my mind, she was as confused as I.

We went to the Church Center at United Nations for a meditation service with Sri Chimnoy. Everybody looked well-heeled. Sri Chimnoy came in. He looked like an Indian banker with a warm loaf in the bank. His smile was boundlessly sincere and love-filled. He shucked a Chesterfield and stood behind a marble dais in pinkgrapefruit robes, bald, silent, glittering. The room was not crowded. He gazed directly at each of us, drilling each with the same stunning glitter. His love-sleepy eyes saucered and the pupils spun. The sheer wet flowing glitter melted me and then his eyeballs rolled white, lifting me like a canary in his palm, his self-loving lips stretching like a cat about to lick its whiskers. The eyeballs descended on Irene and his starlight poured.

"I was swimming!" she said outside. "I mean the mind *swims!*"

We went on to the First International Psychic Film Festival and saw over sixty films in a week. Here again was Sri Chimnoy glittering in the woods. And happy dropouts around the country, meditating on the sun. More bloody psychic surgeons. An astronaut on the moon sending back telepathic messages. Healers, a legitimate English exorcist *binding* bad spirits (he'd SHAKE them out of the sick person's head), cripples made to walk, arthritic hands opening fully. We found ourselves ideally mated by the stars, Leo-Aries, Aries-Leo. We saw the first moving pictures of flashing fingertip aura (our faith in auras rose electrically), a Russian lady who moved pens or piles of matches by mental power, we watched Uri Geller perform a flawless series of clairvoyant feats in the Stamford Research Lab. There was a hideous document about Brazilian Black magic, with live dogs beheaded by hand and hexes that struck like a blowgun (an X-ray showed a woman filled with needles). We watched a Black shaman float himself three feet off the ground three times. A man raised from the dead by the Indian saint Sai Baba was interviewed—he'd been delivered to the morgue and toe-tagged. More moving than all the films about gurus, psychics and saints were six long interviews with Jung, whose lancing intuitions far outshone the God-is-love messages of Easterners—he appeared even more fulfilled than the miracle-working Sai Baba.

And there was a subliminal color film of floating love-forms whose expanding circles shot right at us and caused semi-orgasm—this was set to Isolde's Lovedeath aria from *Tristan*. I recalled with a pang Cynara's rapture at the Met. Then I thought twice about the pang. Was she sitting wideeyed in the empty seat beside me? The pang became a soft electric charge in my groin.

We dined with a festival official who was also a master numer-ologist and a fountain of psychic news—he'd prescreened four hundred mindblowing films from around the globe. Charming and playfully shy, his supercharged spirit popped at the scope of his films. He gave us "dime store" readings of our hidden lives as revealed by our personal numbers. The numbers said I was a Master who came from sturdy burgher stock and had no psychic ability—I saw so far into the future that I had no psychic pres-ent. (A few days later Irene phoned a lady numerologist and went for a two-hour reading to compare numerologists. We found numerology hypnotic in its total focus on oneself. It's not often that somebody will sit and talk about you, and only you, for two hours—in vast detail. Irene began dreaming in numbers and had to phone her numerologist for snap insights: "*There were two sev-ens and an eight and a one, two nines and a five!*")

She pumped him about reincarnation—perhaps after four hundred psychic films he knew something. He said that he hadn't decided, then went on to talk about it and gave a most involved and convincing practical analysis of the energies needed for moving the self through various bodies, and ended by saying that the technical command was almost at hand for controlling large populations through subliminal signals and waves from a central station—that fear and happiness frequencies are already in use in movies and advertising. One festival film had induced the taste of copper in all the judges' mouths. He sat back, pale and stoned, fingers clutching an unseen crystal ball.

"Vibrations are real! Our systems respond irresistibly, even when we know we're being hit. There's no defense—there's frequency that can make your bowels evacuate. The air is full of psychic vampires. I meet and avoid them all day long. They're energy leeches. But post-material man is here and moving into the Psychic Age. The numbers say this is the year of the Announcement."

"The Avatar is climbing over the wall?" I asked.

He smiled, violet eyes popping. "Who am I to say?"

Irene was disturbed. A great urge to mow grass under free blue skies filled me.

We packed and drove to Cape Cod. Almost at earthlevel a white moon blazed unbearably bright in a blue tunnel to another plane. We arrived past midnight. Ocean breezes made shallow music in our giant elm, the waving gargantuan bush an antenna recharging us with unspeakable peace, cellular and sensual. Irene sat for an hour under our rising new willow, its long limbs not drooping but raised like nerves at the moon.

She came in. "I'm sane again. Released!"

"Let me check your birthmarks."

Beyond our bedroom window the elm rushed, flooding us with a spirit-loosening limber roar, a great sliding of shells and shale.

A white cat walked over bedsheets of moonstruck green granite.

Irene switched on her lamp for another chapter in the Krishnamurti biography. "I've got to find out if he renounces the Masters and his occult experiences! How can I sleep?"

"You know what he'll say—the *unknown* cannot be known

through the known. Knowledge distracts from what *is* and only makes new cages. The goal is no goal, only IS in the NOW. Plunge into the IS, my daughter."

"How can you mock Krishnamurti?"

"I love Krishnamurti!"

"He was *there*. And gave it all up—or gave *something* up."

"Right! I'm with you one hundred per cent. I too yearn for perfect tranquillity—you can give me a Peruvian blue sky or California sunset any day."

"The mind not always racing would be nice, you know. *I* is Now."

"Right away. Well, I is under this eiderdown. So goodnight."

"Don't forget to remind yourself." She clicked her battery-powered Nightwriter pen on and off.

"Thanks." I reminded myself to write down my dreams. We'd also bought two luminous writingboards which glowed green through the night. I bounded into myself like a dog.

Suddenly Cynara was lying by and fondling me. My sex shrank, then heaved up. Despite everything, I was skeptical that this was happening. I dismissed the white cat. And these sex-feelings were homemade. Like Krishnamurti, I would not surrender to this grossness. Then her presence made complete entrance into the length of my being, something like an infusion of static-filled silk, my jaw dropped, and the breath shot out of me. But I was awake, and Irene at her book made me most guilty. I told *her* to move down the bed.

She sat on my calves, smiling at me through my closed lids.

I felt that my prayers were really helping her, but I'd forgotten to bless her this night or ask for good works in my sleep. Now I was balanced on a sharp edge, unwilling even to think of driving her off. I remained blank as possible. But a second guilt played over me, that my attentions were keeping her from growing. She was behaving exactly in character—her old character that had killed her. Wanting and not wanting her—don't think of the headwound, don't think of her years in the lowest astral darkness, *eat this spoonful of syphilitic ice cream the Black girl held out!*—ah, I smarted all over.

Something about me moved her to sit on the bureau.

She hovered over us.

She lay between us, smiling.

Irene turned out the light. She entered Irene, who did not know it. Nor did I for a while. Then Irene traced her finger down my nose, and the great elm's roar foamed over us.

I was still, still skeptical! These images and feelings were not necessarily Cynara.

And then I was answered.

Or plunged into her true state at that moment. A dark emerald light was suddenly vividly *there*, green bands of swirling glass twisting into themselves, musically as smoke, glowing on darkness. A veil was rent. Her astral form, intensely beautiful, changeable, turned before me. I felt awe. And again, the peace and power of answered prayer. Had I not longed nightly to see her in the image by which she knew herself?

During the night I felt a strange itch in my crotch. I saw tiny, tiny fruit flies coming out of the pores. Larvae hatched under my skin and wriggled out. I could hardly believe it. Then baby houseflies started pulling themselves out and flying away. My pores looked like a plucked goose. I watched about ten flies, one after another, pull themselves wetly from one favored, tight pore. Never a dream like this before! It was indeed a warning. I never felt more like angel, man and beast, lust as rich as love bound into one being, and Satan himself struggling to be born in every pore.

Chapter Last

She did not come again for three nights.

Our cottage tenant, a divorced friend of Irene's, stopped by for tea and told us about being sick once and finding herself floating against the ceiling. She was quite bosomy and I could not help wondering what her sex life was like in our lonely cottage. What do you do with all that? I must have given off a charge that was picked up by Cynara.

Later I found a psychic listed in the phone book under *Clairvoyants.*

"No!" Irene said. "I know her and don't want to get involved."

"Maybe she could pull in Madame Blavatsky."

"She couldn't pull in Provincetown. I suppose you'd want to bring in Cynara too."

"Oh no! Not after what she did to Roberta Winters. But an alternate reading might be valuable."

She moved naked over the twilight field between the cottage and our house. I had no thought of resistance and met her somewhere on the moonlit lawn. She came as our neighbor but it was her body, as I recognized by intuition next afternoon. She seduced me fully, but without coupling in the earthly manner—

no tingling genitals, but soul bliss and merging that was first awakened by the moonlight on her white nakedness and breasts and then became a marriage of velvet energies and gave a long deep wavery burst without wetness. It was sex in the breast, a rising *chirr* that became a rich heavenly sharing of deepest fellow-feeling the breast could give, and receive, and give.

Her body, the face shadowed by brightness, and yet it was also Irene's form. She had seen my longing to be faithful, especially regarding herself. Somehow she had shaped herself not only to our neighbor and Irene but also to my memory of her own shapeliness.

I brought up the clairvoyant again.

"I am not going to see her," Irene said. And I don't think you should either. We've been warned not to go to readings unless the psychic is personally recommended. I don't see why you're insisting."

I looked left and right.

"And I think you should leave your suicided friends alone. But that's up to you."

"You're right."

"You don't know what you're getting into. Praying is what they need—not calling them back! I get the creeps just thinking about it. It's dangerous to everybody you involve."

A moon like pink flesh detached and rose from far dunes. The blue summer evening darkened and a drumming came from the nearby stables of a horse ridden for a last twilight canter. I had been watching, on and off, a fourteen-year-old ride for the past hour, her long flat dark hair jerking in an electric sheen. We sat and read aloud—on the Buddhic plane at last . . .

That night she came as our next-door neighbor in the Village, whose body again disguised her by its similarity and kept me from sullying Irene's vision of our future marriages up the ladder to Union. Thirty or forty more years in our present vehicles was only a starter. As for Cynara, whatever she was giving she gave it in guises, knowing that if I recognized my astral partner I might force myself to give her up.

Back in the Village I got out my hundreds of pictures, the movie of her, the first Roberta Winters tape and spent the afternoon trying to come to a decision about myself. She did not show up until I ran the movie. I felt her beside me, watching the flaming, gowned figure of the supreme tease shot on the wall, and those questioning haunted eyes as she held up the cat. She was still excited by long tracts about herself.

That night she came as my sister. Again I was fooled by the likeness to Irene, but this time I was not up to such a memory the next day, nor could I bear the desperate imploring I sensed in her repeated seductions.

I lay down to rest at noon, dropping steadily under. *Whoosh*, a hot smoky fire burst beside me under the coffee table where her film lay, a fire vivider than real fire—liquid bronze flames from beyond. This goaded my guilt more violently than my fruit-flies foreboding.

I played the tape we'd made of a healing service the last day of the Spiritualists convention. It was the climactic event and took place in a large auditorium filled to the walls. First there'd been an hour-length TV film about Stonehenge, with terrific sleep-making powers. We sat in the third row but neither of us could stay awake. At last the service began. A middle-aged psychic who was like the mother of a Boston Bird and Garden society, led the meeting. Then a famous healer, who also sold taped messages of wisdom from the Masters, lined up the whole front of the auditorium with fifteen distinguished psychics to perform the service. The audience was invited one at a time to be healed. This was perhaps the most powerful phalanx of healers ever seen in one place, but the speaker made clear that they were not personally responsible for healings—they were only channels for the Holy Spirit to flow through.

There was muted singing of *Alleluia, alleluia* by all, over and over, and no souped-up feeling of the revival tent. It was indeed so muted and reverential that we wondered how it could work its wonders. But a deep chord, stronger than hysteria, rose in waves and folks going down the aisle and standing before the healers responded strongly—so strongly that the healed were fainting left and right down front and being caught by special "catchers" waiting for the falling bodies.

And fall they did, but never hard. The fainters first could be seen weaving stiffly in place. None was failed by a catcher, but was lowered gently to the floor both by healer and catcher. Those who fainted soon revived, were helped up and walked away— they were often strong young people you wouldn't expect to faint, and who were very, very surprised indeed. They were not all confirmed psychic believers. But the Spirit came through its channel, made no distinction, and away they dropped.

We were invited forward but said no. After forty minutes

most of the auditorium had passed before the murmuring healers wiping away at auras or sometimes just clapping a person's
shoulders for a deep eye-contact channel for the Force. Or for
a long, whispered message. Each psychic worked differently. I
changed my mind and stepped before a handsome bearded healer
in blue denim. He looked like a ballplayer. To my left, Roberta
Winters in a shining blue gown worked on a lad in a wheelchair,
her blue eyes charged with hope. I was happy for her to see me in
the lineup, and delighted to be there.

"What are you here for?" the ballplayer asked, grinning.

"I'm great. I'm just here."

"Just in general, huh?" He laughed, spirit simmering.

"Well, maybe for an ulcer that I used to have and don't want
back." Actually, it sounded too dumb to say I was standing in for
my mother's ulcer.

"No, no ulcer, you're in great health." He looked at my aura.
"We'll just take away those negative feelings you have here and
there."

"Great."

"Look at my palm. See that black dot in the center?" He held
his palm before my eyes. "Look hard. See that black dot, that's all
your negative feelings."

I stared at his empty palm and a mystic haze rose from my
stomach to my eyes. I was so surprised I couldn't focus.

"Now watch that dot. You see it?"

"Mm!"

He began drawing his palm away. "I'm going to draw off all
your negativity—*pop it!*—and it's gonna go away. Right? Watch

that dot, watch it, *watch it*—" Suddenly he slapped his palm with the other hand. "It's gone! Feel better?" What a Zen hurler!

"Oh yes." But I wasn't so sure it was showing in my aura, since I'd hedged on smoking and my food plan.

I went back to Irene, who smiled in the currents flowing about. People we'd been seeing or talking with all weekend were suddenly flat on their backs. "Go ahead," I said. Irene went to Roberta Winters.

"Do you have anything for me to work on?"

"My tension."

Roberta Winters shone with caring as she reached behind and pressed the vertebrae above the small of Irene's back. A soft charge rushed up Irene's spine. Her nerves brightened throughout and her eyes prickled. She returned near tears.

A catcher turned to me and asked, "Would you take my place? I been standing here a long time."

I moved in front of a healer who looked like an old gipsy lady—and talked a lot like one. A Jewish man with reddish curls moved between us and she began talking with him while I stood ready to catch. I felt great. My motto is *Fear No Ridicule*.

They mumbled together a while, then she began speaking more loudly. "Don't worry about being a Jew! There's only one truth, one church, one religion. You are a temple. Accept the Spirit!"

I had my hands at his waist and did some aura cleaning with a full heart, directing my own energy straight into his spine. But he was sturdy and not a fainter. He finally thanked her and walked away pale, wideeyed and damply moved.

154

I watched Roberta Winters beside me, her blue power rippling as a man wavered before her. She shone. The lad in the wheelchair sat aside, talking to his legs and attuning them to spiritual nerves. Energy hung in the air, waiting to bolt into skeptic or believer alike.

My gipsy and I received the last person to be healed, the Fat Man in a Blue Suit, whose grotesque comments I'd been hearing for three days. He stood before her, settling his shoulder bag onto a chair, and I raised my hands to his vast waist. He was well over four hundred pounds and unpleasant as a gorged leech.

"What's wrong with you?" she asked.

"Whatta ya think's wrong?"

"You're too fat. You gotta get unfat. Listen to me!" And she launched into a very personal healing and not quietly.

I tried not to listen while pouring my heaviest energies into his blue bulk, unscumming his aura, and with utmost concentration telling him to love himself. Then I tried to zap him into joining Overeaters Anonymous and getting some friendship into his life.

He sank slowly, shocking me, but only clipped some tissues out of his shoulder bag. He wiped his eyes, then began shaking and reeling, and sank as I shot my arms around him. I saw the gipsy's triumph—she'd opened the widest channel she had—as I went down under him, breaking his fall. I got to my feet. His large mouth was open and at peace.

"That'll wake him up!" she told me. Other healers looked at her in dismay, even shushing her, but she only said, "Well, the brute needs all the help he can get, for God's sake."

He woke up, looking about. I helped him up. He looked straight into me and said, "Mass hypnosis. They do it with mass hypnosis."

It was over. I heaved a smile at Roberta Winters and went back to Irene. She gripped me, glowing.

The tape ended. I picked up a picture of Cynara taken by her husband five minutes after she'd delivered her daughter. She lay holding the baby up and grinning straight into the lens. It was the greatest moment of her life. She had for a brief flash conquered her shadows. Her face is wiped and waterfresh, the dark eyes ringed, white and joyous. She smiles like a batter who has just driven in three runs and crossed home plate himself. It is not simply self-forgiveness for all her failings, it is sheer victory.

That day I still could not bear to tell her to leave. I only asked her to work on herself, and to accept help, and I asked God to bless her. But she read what I did not say, did not even allow myself to think. When she did not appear for two weeks, and I did not feel her presence, not vividly, night or day, I knew she was at last at work on her recovery. And as a kind friend had given me peace.

Last night, unbidden, I saw the last of her for a very long time, I think. As I sank pictureless to sleep, an image rose and was held before me of a brown clay mask in a brown starlight swirl. I was stunned by the mask's earthen dullness—the deadness of a death mask. Only today do I understand that it is not a death mask but a being seen as a death mask, an image of all the earth she owns, shown for my good by her Helpers, or by mine. Or perhaps by her, in some unknown way. She is asleep. Spirits do rest for great efforts. If you have a spare blessing, send it to her—give my book real purpose. When the dead awaken, they need every prayer they can get.

THE END

October 6, 1975
Greenwich Village
Cape Cod

Acknowledgments

Thanks to the following for their generous financial support which helped to defray some of this publication's production costs:

Thomas Young Barmore Jr, Sam Bertram, Matthew Boe,
Brian R. Boisvert, Dy Booth, Lee Broadmore, Michael Broder,
Scott Chiddister, Sarah Chinn, Eric L. Collette,
Parker & Malcolm Curtis, Tom Davidson, dcmalone,
Joshua Doughty, Craig Duckett, Isaac Ehrlich, Nathan Friedman,
Steve Fuller, E Gaustad, GMarkC, Jason Gray, Adam Gregory,
Everett Haagsma, Per Kristian Hoff, Dave Holets,
Jacob Tarner Howard, Conor Hultman, Martin Jarvis,
Fred W Johnson, Jacob H Joseph, Christopher Klein,
Kurt Johann Klemm, Sergey Kochergan, Stefan Kruger,
Leonore the Wanderer, Nick Long, Marcel, Jim McElroy,
Jack Mearns, Sergio Méndez-Torres, Tim Mentuis, Jason H Miller,
Jody Mock, Spencer F Montgomery, Gregory Moses, Scott Murphy,
Clyde Nads, Richard Novak, Michael O'Shaughnessy,
Andrew Pearson, Julie Phillips, Pedro Ponce, Waylon M. Prince,
Judith Redding, Robert Riley-Mercado, Owen Rowe,
Stephen M. Tabler, Elisa Townshend, Ted Travelstead, Tim Tucker,
William Waters, Christopher Wheeling, Isaiah Whisner,
T.R. Wolfe, The Zemenides Family, and Anonymous